BIRDS of PREY

By Leon Augustus Hausman

Leon Augustus Hausman

BIRDS of PREY

of Northeastern North America

ILLUSTRATED IN PEN AND INK BY

Jacob Bates Abbot

Peterborough · New Hampshire

RICHARD · R · SMITH · PUBLISHERS

1966

SECOND EDITION, REVISED AND ENLARGED

This book is set in Linotype Baskerville
and printed on Monadnock Paper
at the Colonial Press Inc., Clinton, Massachusetts
MANUFACTURED IN THE UNITED STATES OF AMERICA

To

Arthur Augustus Allen,

LOVER, PROTECTOR, AND STUDENT OF BIRDS;

PROFESSOR OF ORNITHOLOGY;

AND STAUNCH FRIEND.

1384265

A WORD TO THE READER

THE INTELLECTUAL and aesthetic profit derived from watching birds far outweighs the pleasure of killing them. This in itself would constitute a sufficient reason for the protection of that great assemblage of birds whose members form so picturesque an element in our skies—the so-called *birds of prey*. We say "so-called" because, as will later appear, this phrase is an inappropriate one to apply only to hawks and owls. Most birds prey upon other forms of animal life and hence are equally "birds of prey."

There is still another reason for extending our protection to the hawks and owls. Within comparatively recent years the substantial value of our raptorial birds as regulators of avine eugenics has come generally to be appreciated by the reading public. It is incontestably established upon the firmest scientific basis that the raptorial birds, in destroying weak and unfit individuals among birds and other creatures, are performing the unquestionably valuable service of helping indirectly to insure the permanence and propagation of only the strongest and most vigorous individuals of those groups upon which they prey. In the long run it is chiefly the less strong, the less active, the less generally capable, and especially the decidedly weak and ailing individuals which fall prey to hawks and owls. The breeding stock of the supply is thus purged of its least desirable members. The term "predator," so long applied to our birds of prey as an epithet of disparagement, is now increasingly regarded as a term expressing our approbation of the service these birds are rendering. The expressions "vermin" and "scourge,"

ix

when applied to birds of prey, are now quite out of fashion among studious folk, and are being replaced by such terms as "regulators," "genetic controllers," and the like. In using such titles we have in mind the larger biological aspects of the matter, and are not speaking in immediate terms.

On the other hand, it is undeniable that in some regions birds of prey may often become troublesome and should be destroyed or reduced in their numbers. There is a reasonable local control to be wisely exercised. Indeed, man may invoke the express command of Holy Scripture to "replenish the earth and subdue it, and have dominion over the fish of the sea and over the fowls of the air, and over every living thing that moveth upon the earth." But *in their rightful habitat* the birds of prey, so estimable an element of beauty and natural interest, and so valuable a factor in the biological balance, should be molested no more than any other natural group. State and Federal laws, now protecting many of our native birds of prey, bear witness to our rapidly growing recognition of their worth. Sportsmen, game breeders, game wardens, farmers, and all students of wild life who keep abreast of the constant march of biological learning, act in accordance with their knowledge.

The hunting habits of the birds of prey have often been called cruel, blood-thirsty, ferocious, or ruthless. But all these terms carry a moral implication. Any juridical observations of this sort start on the presumptive ground that birds are accountable to a human ethical code, whereas the simple physiological fact is that a hungry bird secures its meal after the only mode of action of which it is capable. Birds of prey do not hunt for the joy of hunting, nor kill for the joy of killing, but only because these instinctive activities are necessary to satisfy the primal need for food.

When one scrutinizes the explicit act of slaughter itself, it is not "cruel" in the sense of being malicious, protracted, nor in most instances even productive of great pain. A bird of prey stooping upon its quarry grips it once, powerfully, and thus drives its long, curved talons, sharp as daggers, into the very vitals; or else with its hard, half-clenched fist strikes the quarry a mighty buffet in mid-air which carries instant death. Nature has not devised any methods for the slaughter of animals for food more merciful than these. Neither do birds of prey wound their victims and permit them to crawl away into hiding, there to undergo the pangs of a lonely and protracted dissolution. We human beings might take a lesson from the birds of prey.

Any bird which feeds upon a smaller and weaker creature is equally a bird of prey. From the biologist's point of view, a hawk which swoops upon a pheasant, and a bluebird which pounces upon a beetle, are sisters under the skin. And what more complete and devastating example could one desire of all that is derogatory in the phrase "birds of prey" than Man, that rapacious species known to science as *Homo sapiens,* whom Plato defined as a "featherless biped" and whom the Psalmist described as "a little lower than the angels"?

L.A.H.

ACKNOWLEDGMENTS

I AM A PART of all that I have met." The materials of this volume have been drawn from the writer's many field notebooks, kept regularly ever since he was a boy of ten in a Connecticut town, preserving his observations in growing detail from all the northeastern states, particularly New England, New York, and New Jersey. He has also learned much from excellent writers on our native bird life whose works are listed in the bibliography at the end of this volume. The writer is deeply indebted to Dr. Arthur A. Allen and Dr. Elsa G. Allen, both of Cornell University, who read various parts of the manuscript with critical eyes; to the late Jacob Bates Abbott whose facile pen delineated our native birds of prey in such a lively, artistic, and anatomically accurate manner; to Dr. William H. Martin, Dean of the College of Agriculture and Director of the New Jersey State Agricultural Experiment Station, Rutgers University, for aid in reproducing Mr. Abbott's drawings; and to Mr. Roger DeBaun, former editor at the Agricultural Experiment Station at Rutgers University, for his assistance in reading various parts of the manuscript.

May I here pay tribute to my father and mother, true lovers of nature, who by precept and example first taught me the basic lessons of forbearance toward the lesser brethren of the forest; who taught me when in field and woodland to protect rather than to destroy, to reflect upon rather than to kill; and who equipped me

xiii

early in childhood with field glass, camera, and notebook rather than with dog, gun, and gamebag.

The author is indebted also to various publishers and authors for their permission to reproduce copyrighted or original material: from Bailey's *Handbook of Birds of the Western United States*, Houghton Mifflin Company; Fisher's *Hawks and Owls from the Standpoint of the Farmer*, United States Wildlife Service; Louis J. Halle's *Birds Against Men*, The Viking Press; *Useful Birds and Their Protection* and *Birds of Massachusetts and Other New England States*, Office of the Secretary, Commonwealth of Massachusetts; Hudson's *British Birds*, Longmans, Green and Company; and Jacob Bates Abbott's "Observations on the Goshawk at Mt. Monadnock," *The Auk*.

In conclusion, my gratitude is especially expressed to my wife, Ethel Hinckley Hausman, my constant companion in field and forest, without whose assistance and infectious enthusiasm my observation and study of nature would be dreary indeed.

L.A.H.

CONTENTS

LIST OF ILLUSTRATIONS

INTRODUCTION

vvvvvvvvvvvvvvvvvvvvvvvvvvvvvvvvvvvvvvvvvvvvvvvvvvvvvvvvvvvvvvvvvvvvvvvvvvvvvvvvv

THE EARLIEST references to birds of prey in the history of mankind are those relating to the eagles which, with hawks and other birds, figured prominently in the complex systems of early Roman ornithomancy or ceremonial divination from birds. Here one finds directions for intricate procedures to foretell future events or regulate religious rituals by the actions of birds or by the condition of their penetralia. One group of priests called the *augurs* (a word meaning "bird talk") listened to what birds had to say; another group termed the *auspices* (a word meaning "bird viewers") observed their motions, particularly the migrational movements of the larger birds such as cranes, hawks, storks, eagles, and vultures, or examined the condition of the organs of the viscera, or recorded the activities, especially the eating, of the "sacred chickens" of the temple.

The use of birds of prey for hunting, or the art of falconry, is depicted in the frescoes and sculptures of the early peoples of the Tigris-Euphrates Valley and of the early Egyptians; the sport was developed in the very earliest times among the peoples of India and northern Africa. During the Middle Ages falconry became the sport of kings, prelates, and great nobles. Within recent years it has been revived, especially in England, and to a less extent in America, particularly in the Genesee Valley in New York.

The comparative sizes of birds of prey are interesting. The smallest of all such birds, to be found among the Pigmy Falcons, or Falconets, of the Eastern Himalayas and Burma, is the little Red-

Legged Falconet (*Microhierax caerulescens*) of Nepal and Siam. This diminutive hawk measures only about five and a half inches in length, which is nearly an inch shorter than our ubiquitous English Sparrow! The title of "largest" seems to be shared equally among three species: the great Andean Condor (*Sarcorhamphus gryphus*), the California Condor (*Gymnogyps californianus*), and the Bearded Vulture or Lammergeier (*Gypaetus barbatus*) of Europe, all of which species may display a wingspread of from nine to twelve feet and attain the surprising weight of something more than twenty-five pounds. A still larger vulture, now extinct, is found as a fossil.

Although the two larger groups of birds of prey, the hawks and owls, are similar in their habits of food capture, ingestion, and pellet formation, and although they exhibit certain similar superficial structural adaptations for their common raptorial habit (in the conformation of beak, wings, and talons), they are not closely related anatomically, and it appears that they could not have been derived from common ancestral forms. Apparently the hawks and their kin are descended from the same primitive group which gave rise to the cranes, whereas the owls show a closer affinity to the Caprimulgiform birds. Familiar examples of these are our native whippoorwills and nighthawks.

With the exception of some of the vultures, birds of prey all feed in a similar manner. After a kill has been made, the smaller creatures such as frogs and salamanders or even shrews and small birds may be swallowed whole. The larger forms are torn into pieces before being bolted. Hawks usually pluck off most of the larger feathers. Within the stomach, the indigestible portions of the meal are rolled into compact pellets and ejected within a short time from the mouth. These pellets, about as large as one's thumb or smaller, depending upon the size of the bird, are composed of fur, feathers, scales, bones, the hard parts of insects, and the like, according to the nature of the bird's customary food. A study of such pellets together with a study of the contents of the crops and stomachs of the birds of prey collected over a large territory and representing all seasons of the year can be supplemented by studies of the feeding habits in the field with binoculars and telescopes. These studies give us a knowledge of the foods of the various species of our birds of prey and leave one in no doubt concerning their economic status.

Young nestling hawks are voracious eaters and require constant feeding from the parents. The older birds eat less often, however, and adult specimens are frequently brought into the laboratory during the winter months with their crops and stomachs entirely empty and contracted. When a generous kill is made after a period of enforced abstinence, they gorge themselves to the point of repletion, an indulgence which is usually followed by a period of sloth and general inactivity.

The eyes of birds of prey are probably the most highly developed organs of vision in the world. They are so large that in most instances the two eyeballs occupy more space in the skull than the brain itself.

The cornea or outermost transparent envelope of the eye is very convex, and its shape can often be altered by many tiny muscles not found in the eyes of other animals. The lens, the image-focusing element of the eye, is also much better supplied with muscles; and the retina, or image-receiving element, is more sensitive. With the power of rapid and delicate focusing, such an eye can be transformed almost instantly from a telescope into a microscope. The eye possesses not two eyelids, but three. The third "lid," known as the nictitating membrane, is located in the inner corner of the eye. This membrane is present also in the human eye, but is reduced to utter uselessness and is represented only by a tiny pulp of pinkish tissue in the inner corner of the eye. In the eyes of birds this nictitating membrane is transparent and can be pulled across the cornea to protect it from dust as well as from high winds which have a tendency to dry off the eyeball. Since the nictitating membrane is transparent, the bird is not temporarily blinded when winking its eyes, a feature of great importance to a creature which must maintain an unbroken lookout for enemies. When asleep, however, a bird closes its eyes as do human beings.

Within the eyeball itself, in the region of the vitreous humor, is located a structure known as the pecten which has long been a puzzle to students of bird anatomy and physiology. It is a soft, spongy, erectile organ projecting forward from the retina near the entrance of the optic nerve into the cavity of the vitreous humor. The pecten is richly supplied with blood capillaries and may serve as an organ to regulate the pressure of the fluids of the eye.

The iris, or iris diaphragm, regulates the diameter of the pupil. It is variously colored in birds—blue, black, brown, or red. In the hawks and owls it is often yellow. Some species may have a brown iris, like the Barred Owl. It is the yellow iris of the Great Horned Owl which gives the eyes of this species their terrifying aspect. An account of the nocturnal "eye-shine" of birds is given on page 109.

The hawks make large nests of sticks, bark, leaves, and like materials placed high in trees, on the ledges of inaccessible cliffs, or as in the case of the Marsh Hawk amid grasses and sedges on the ground. Some nest like the Sparrow Hawk in holes in trees. Often a pair will make use of the deserted nest of some other species of hawk or of a crow or squirrel, remodeling these habitations to fit their needs. Hawks remain mated for long periods of time, possibly for life, and usually return to the same nest year after year. Moreover, they are tender and solicitous parents.

Hawks produce a great variety of notes, of which the most commonly heard are screams or squeals. When these are sufficiently mollified by distance they fall upon the ear with a pleasingly musical, wild, and elemental cadence which brings to mind agreeable memories of tranquil summer days among quiet wooded hills. When in the vicinity of the nest and of the young, hawks give voice to a multiplicity of clucks, murmurs, and other sounds reminiscent of the barnyard; but when the nest is threatened or they themselves are attacked, their utterances become shrill and piercing, or harsh, abrupt, and menacing.

Hawks are generally migratory birds. They do not travel in organized flocks, but straggle along in loose companies, in pairs or singly, making their appearance in the greatest numbers on days when moderate, steady winds aid their buoyant flight. At various places favorable to the development of ancillary currents of air or over regions which form natural geographic routes of travel, observers during the spring and fall may watch hundreds of these stately migrants passing overhead. In mountainous regions, from high elevations, one can often see these great birds passing on a level with the eyes or even below. Some of the favored spots for watching the migration of hawks in our northeastern states are Cape May, New Jersey; Hawk Mountain at Drehersville, Pennsylvania; the sandstone ridges near Deerfield, Massachusetts, culminating in Sugarloaf Mountain near Sunderland; the huge wall of the Brush and Crag Mountain ridge just east of Mount Hermon; the Mount Holyoke–Mount Tom range, and their southward trending chain of high hills to Mount Proven and on into northern Connecticut; and the Meriden Mountains in the southern part of that state. Farther north in the Green Mountains, the White Mountains, and the mountains of Maine there are many favorable places for observation wherever chains of abrupt acclivities of a thousand feet or more rise at such angles to the course of the benign westerly winds that they create upward currents of air. On these the birds are borne aloft with a minimum of flapping—coasting along, as it were, for mile after mile on the way to their wintering grounds farther south and again drifting northward in the spring.

"The migratory passage of birds, like the movements of the stars, can be a great consolation to men whose minds continually search for an established order and progression in the universe. The knowledge that, whatever we may make of ourselves in the moment of our existence, the stars will continue in their appointed courses, the seasons will move in their confirmed order, the birds will pursue their bi-annual migrations, carries with it a sense of ultimate security . . . It seems to give us the intimation of a Will that directs us . . . Order, harmony, regularity, those elements implicit in the flight of birds, are beyond the touch of good and evil that men do in the numbered hours of their survival. Knowledge of the integrated pattern of the universe, in which the birds share . . . secures us from the nightmare of anarchy" *

The significance of the birds of prey to our entire economy is forcibly illustrated by the depredations of rodents to which we would be subjected were it not for the birds. The Meadow Mouse (*Microtus pennsylvanicus pennsylvanicus*), also known as the Field Mouse, Field Vole, or Meadow Vole, and other subspecies merit a word by themselves in any discussion of the habits of our native birds of prey, since mice form such a large proportion of their dietaries, especially those of many of the owls. The Meadow Mouse is interesting not only for this reason, but also because it bears the distinction of being the most numerous mammal on the North American Continent and is one of the most destructive of all nature's forces with which those who produce our foodstuffs have to contend.

Meadow Mice are small, brownish, soft-furred, small-eyed, short-eared, short-tailed little mice, about five to seven inches in over-all length. Over seventy-five species of their genus, *Microtus,* occur in North America. The best-known forms and the ones common in the eastern portion of our country are those of the *pennsylvanicus* group, of which there are about sixteen members. They inhabit meadows, pastures, fields, and any damp ground where grasses and sedges abound. Here they make an intricate pattern of runways—little trails and tunnels through the grass which lead downwards in some places to underground burrows and chambers or end in neat, globular, grassy nests on or near the ground for summer use.

Meadow Mice breed with incredible rapidity. From two to nine young are produced in each litter, and the female is capable of bearing young when only forty-five days old. The period of gestation is only twenty-one days long. Seventeen litters were brought forth by

* Halle, *Birds Against Men.*

one female in captivity, and another had given birth to seventy-eight young before she reached her first birthday! A single pair of these little creatures might easily be responsible for over a million descendants a year were it not for the check imposed upon such multiplication by their natural enemies, principally the hawks and owls. This alone firmly establishes the worth of our birds of prey.

Even supposing there to be as few as ". . . ten Meadow Mice to the acre, then on one hundred acres of meadow these would destroy about eleven tons of grass, or five and a half tons of hay per year, and . . . in the thirty-eight 'mouse states' this would cause a loss of over three million tons of hay per year" (*Bailey*).

But even this is not the whole extent of the damage, for not only do Meadow Mice destroy grass, they also feed voraciously upon roots, bulbs, tubers, twigs, foliage, flowers, seeds, and in addition cause great injury by girdling trees, shrubs, and vines. One can picture the condition which would inevitably ensue if the natural enemies of such creatures were removed or even seriously diminished.

In helping mightily in keeping down the numbers of these noxious forms our native birds of prey perform a very welcome service. The irony of the matter is that the very persons whom the birds benefit sometimes reward their services by vituperation and a charge of shot!

Much concern has been voiced recently about the consequences for our wildlife resulting from the indiscriminate use of chemical sprays and pesticides. The following paragraph, appearing in a 1963 "News Letter" of the Massachusetts Audubon Society, will suffice here to point out the effects on predatory birds: "In the United States it has been noted that a number of birds of prey are declining rapidly—this decline apparently precipitated by the widespread use of pesticides. Although all species of birds of prey are potentially endangered, the following are in real danger of being extinguished: Osprey, Red-Shouldered Hawk, American Bald Eagle, and Peregrine Falcon."

The nomenclature used in this volume is that of the American Ornithologists' Union (referred to as the A.O.U.) in its fifth edition, 1957, of "Check-List of North American Birds."

BIRDS of PREY

```
┌─────────────────────────────────────────────┐
│                                             │
│                   THE                        │
│                                             │
│         AMERICAN VULTURES                    │
│                                             │
│            ( Family Cathartidae )            │
│                                             │
└─────────────────────────────────────────────┘
```

THE

AMERICAN VULTURES

(Family Cathartidae)

VULTURES (sometimes also called buzzards) are large, hawk-like birds, with the head and a portion of the neck devoid of feathers, the skin of these parts being rough and leathery. The bill, while large and heavy, is not sharply hooked, nor are the feet strong and well developed as in the true hawks, and the rather blunt talons are neither very long nor very curved and hence are ill-adapted for seizing and holding food. In fact our native vultures seldom put their feet upon their food to hold it (though this may differ with the individual), but seize it in their beaks and shuffle backwards along the ground, twitching their heads this way and that in their attempts to wrench off pieces large enough to swallow.

Their food consists of carrion, often in an advanced state of putrescence. They seldom attack living creatures except those that are weak and feeble or upon the point of death, although there are a few records of their attacks upon others.

The wings of vultures are long, broad, and strong. The muscles

1

attached to the keel of the sternum are thick and robust, giving unusual powers of sustained flight. From great heights or near the ground, vultures detect their food by sight and not by smell, as was formerly supposed, for although the external openings of the nostrils are large, yet the mucous membranes of the nose are not well expanded; the olfactory nerves and the olfactory lobes of the brain show no extraordinary degree of development such as would indicate keen sense of smell. Experiments in the field have failed to establish conclusively any unusually acute olfactory abilities.

Vultures are almost voiceless birds. The muscles of the syrinx or voice box are reduced or lacking, and the only sounds produced are hoarse grunts and hisses which carry only for short distances.

When attacked, vultures often spew forth at the offender a malodorous mass from the crop—an extremely effective means of defense. The young birds are frequently fed by having this same loathsome substance regurgitated into their open mouths by the parents.

The name of the New World family of vultures, *Cathartidae,* is derived from the Greek *cathartes,* signifying "a cleanser," and indicates the birds' habit of keeping the fields and woods free from decomposing animal remains.

There are three species of North American vultures of which two, the Turkey Vulture (*Cathartes aura septentrionalis*) and the Black Vulture (*Coragyps atratus atratus*) , occur in the eastern portion of the United States.

1

Turkey Vulture

wwwwwwwwwwwwwwwwwwwwwwwwwwwwwwwwwwwwwwwwwwwwwwwwww

CATHARTES AURA SEPTENTRIONALIS

ALSO CALLED

Turkey Buzzard, Red-Headed Buzzard

ADULTS Head and neck naked, the skin and area about the base of the bill bright red. Rest of body covered with plumage which is black or blackish, the feathers edged with grayish-brown.

YOUNG Similar to the adults, but having the head covered with soft grayish-brown feathers.

BODY LENGTH	*WINGSPREAD*
26 to 32 inches	68 to 72 inches

The Turkey Vulture is a paradox among birds. The embodiment of grace and majesty in the air, it becomes, on the ground, an uncouth and loutish object, unseemly alike in appearance and in habits.

No bird navigates the currents of the upper air with more regal assurance than does the vulture as with set and motionless pinions it ascends in ever-widening spirals until it becomes all but lost in the blue vault above. But though it rises "to heaven or near it," the bird pours forth no "profuse strains of unpremeditated art." Its elevation of body is seemingly unaccompanied by any corresponding exaltation of mind; its attention is still fixed upon the earth beneath as its keen eyes scrutinize the fields far below for any indi-

3

cation of dead or dying animals which constitute its food. Longfellow, in his *Song of Hiawatha* has perfectly described the gather-
ing of vultures for their grim repast:

> "Never stoops the soaring vulture
> On his quarry in the desert,
> On the sick or wounded bison,
> But another vulture, watching
> From his high aërial lookout,
> Sees the downward plunge, and follows;
> And a third pursues the second,
> Coming from the invisible ether,
> First a speck, and then a vulture,
> Till the air is dark with pinions."

The value of the Turkey Vulture results from its consumption of
carrion which would otherwise befoul the fields. In places where
the birds are numerous they thus constitute a most efficient corps of
scavengers. The soft, decayed flesh is rent apart by the beak, the feet
being so small and weak that they are seldom or never used to hold
down the morsel during feeding. Living creatures are not often
disturbed, though weak or half-dead individuals may sometimes
be set upon and killed. Turkey Vultures gorge themselves with such
violence and to such repletion as often to be incapable of rising
from the ground in flight until they have regurgitated a large part
of their filthy load. They are the chief gluttons of the bird world,
and like Athelstane of Coningsburgh, seem to have "no pleasure
save to fill, to swill and to call for more."

That the Turkey Vulture occasionally attacks helpless young animals is indicated by the graphic account which W. J. Hamilton, Jr.
gives in *The Auk,* July, 1941: "During March, 1939, at Half-Way
Lodge, fifteen miles east of Fort Myers, Florida, Mr. Dwight Dyess
witnessed buzzards successfully attacking and killing young pigs.
Several new-born litters were destroyed by these birds. On one occasion the birds boldly approached the young shortly after the sow
had farrowed them, and tore at the umbilical cord and belly, dis-

5

embowelling the little pigs. Although the sow was but a few feet off, she offered no resistance other than a few passive grunts."

Turkey Vultures make no nest—in this respect they are unique among our hawks. The eggs are deposited in a depression on the ground or between rocks or in the cavity of a decayed stump. Dense woods, or second growth, with rocks are the localities frequently chosen.

The Turkey Vulture may be identified in flight by its great expanse of wing, for it possesses the greatest wingspread of any of our native eastern birds except the Bald and Golden Eagles. When soaring, vultures hold their wings slightly upward at an obtuse angle, whereas eagles hold theirs outward at almost a straight angle. The rounded, narrow tail of the vulture is not spread broadly fanwise in flight, and the light, reflected from the somewhat glossy plumage, often imparts to the birds a silvery hue, particularly along the outer edge of the under surface of the wings. The head is seen to be red only at short range.

The Turkey Vulture has been called a "voiceless bird." However it frequently utters a subdued grunt, and when angry, a prolonged hiss, somewhat like a gander.

The Turkey Vulture is common in southern and central New Jersey, but as one proceeds northwards the birds become progressively scarcer. In southern and eastern New York and Connecticut they are to be seen only infrequently, while in the north they are recorded only as rare stragglers. An interesting notation on the apparently increasing frequency of the Turkey Vulture in New England has been contributed by Samuel A. Eliot, Jr., of Smith College, Northampton, Massachusetts (*The Auk*, July 1, 1941): "On August 19, 1941, while motoring through Halifax and Whitingham, Vermont, I saw near the village of Jacksonville, about three miles north of the Massachusetts line, a Turkey Vulture (*Cathartes aura septentrionalis*) flying westward slowly and unmistakably. Perhaps it was the same wandering bird that had been seen at Pelham, Massachusetts, August 4 (Margaret Morse Nice) and Squam

Lake, New Hampshire, August 10 (K. W. Burke). Only two Vermont records were given by Forbush in his *Birds of Massachusetts and Other New England States* . . . and only four—and of these only one is complete with date, locality, and observer's name—are known even now to Wendell P. Smith, the State Ornithologist. But in recent years, principally in late April, the species has been seen remarkably often in western Massachusetts, and one can predict that it will visit southern Vermont more and more frequently."

2

Black Vulture

~~~~~~

CORAGYPS ATRATUS ATRATUS

ALSO CALLED
Black Buzzard, Carrion Crow, Jim Crow

ADULTS Head and neck naked, the skin and area about the base of the bill black or dusky. Rest of the body covered with shining black plumage. A large whitish patch near the ends of the wings at the base of the primaries.

YOUNG Similar to the adults, but lacking the glossy sheen of the plumage.

BODY LENGTH	*WINGSPREAD*
24 to 27 inches	54 to 59 inches

The Black Vulture is a slightly smaller edition of the Turkey Vulture, possessing smaller and weaker beak and feet and lacking the red head. The Black Vulture's food consists of much softer and much fouler substance than that of its larger relative, the bird usually filling itself to the point of distention upon carrion and offal in the most advanced stages of putrefaction and being attracted even by ordure. The writer has often seen flocks of these birds in the Deep South gorging themselves upon the decomposing bodies of domestic animals which had been dragged into an open field, filling their crops with the most loathsome putrescence. "Food?" grunted an old negro contemptuously to whom I had spoken about the feed-

9

ing habits of the Black Vulture, "Dose birds don't eat *food;* dey eats *rot!*"

The Black Vulture is a bird of the southern states very rarely straggling north of the southern tip of New Jersey. The few records that exist since 1877 are from the central and southern portions of the territory.

In flight the wings of the Black Vulture are seen to be shorter and broader than those of the Turkey Vulture and show a broad patch of grayish white near their ends at the base of the long primaries. The tail is short and square across its end. Black Vultures soar less than their larger relatives and alternate their periods of gliding by flapping their wings vigorously. These characteristics make the identification of the Black Vulture possible almost as far as the bird can be seen in the sky. When perched, it may be identified by the black instead of the red head.

THE AMERICAN HAWKS, EAGLES, AND THEIR KIN

(Families Accipitridae and Falconidae)

THE hawks and their kin differ externally from the vultures chiefly in possessing heads thickly invested with feathers; strongly hooked and very sharp bills; and long, curved, strong, sharp talons set upon large, powerful, tuberculated toes. The middle portion or tibio-tarsus of the leg is thickly clothed with feathers which project well beyond the carpal or "heel" joint. The knee of a hawk's leg is seldom exposed except when the bird is reaching out its leg to its utmost extent (*see* illustration of the Red-Shouldered Hawk facing page 34).

There are some fifty-five species and subspecies of the families *Accipitridae* and *Falconidae* in North America, of which about twenty occur in our northeastern states.

11

3
Swallow-Tailed Kite

〰〰〰〰〰〰〰〰〰〰〰〰〰〰〰〰〰〰〰〰〰〰〰〰〰〰〰〰〰〰〰〰〰〰〰〰〰〰〰

ELANOIDES FORFICATUS FORFICATUS

ALSO CALLED
Forked-Tailed Kite, Swallow Hawk,
Wasp Hawk, Snake Hawk

ADULTS Whole of head, neck, rump, under parts, and lining of wings, pure white. Upper parts black, iridescent with sheens of bronze, purplish, and green. Wings very long, narrow, pointed, and crescentic and, when folded over the back, extending to the tip of the tail. Tail very long, slender, and deeply forked—whole contour of bird like an exaggerated Barn Swallow.

YOUNG Similar to the adults but duller and with less iridescence. Head and neck bearing fine dusky streaks. Long flight feathers of the wing and feathers of the tail very narrowly tipped with white.

BODY LENGTH	*WINGSPREAD*
19½ to 25½ inches	45 to 50 inches

Female somewhat larger than the male.

This aristocratic and beautiful species somewhat resembles an enormous Barn Swallow both in its contour and flight, and these characteristics together with its striking black and white plumage render it unmistakable in the field, either awing or at rest. It often soars and circles high into the air or dashes erratically here and

there over the tops of trees and bushes or meadows and ponds, and is held by some to be unquestionably the most graceful bird on the continent. Unfortunately it is only an accidental straggler except in the South, and even there it is becoming so rare as to be threatened with extermination. There are only some dozen or so records of the bird's visits to the northeastern states. Wherever it has appeared, it has evoked a burst of ornithological panegyrics. William Brewster gives one of the finest descriptions of its flight: "For a moment it floats motionless, as if suspended by an invisible wire; the next, it glides close to the ground, crossing and re-crossing every foot of space. The long, thin wings, firmly set, cleave the air like knife blades, and the forked tail, spread to its fullest, is inclined to one side or the other as the bird changes its swift course. Finally rising to the level of the tree tops it is gone as it came, like a beautiful vision."

The Swallow-Tailed Kite feeds upon beetles, moths, locusts, dragonflies, crickets, wasps, caterpillars, and other large insects, and to a less extent upon reptiles and frogs. Many of the insects are captured in the air by the dexterous birds, since they often feed after the manner of swallows. Birds and mammals are not represented in its diet.

Concerning both the Swallow-Tailed and the White-Tailed Kites, John Bichard May very justly points out that "there is no possible excuse for killing such harmless and easily recognized birds, for their feeding habits have been well known since the days of Wilson and Audubon."

4

Eastern Goshawk

～～～～～～～～～～～～～～～～～～～～～～～～～～～～～～～～～

ACCIPITER GENTILIS ATRICAPILLUS

ALSO CALLED

Partridge Hawk, Blue Hen Hawk, Blue Darter,
Chicken Hawk, Blue Hawk, Dove Hawk,
Blue Partridge Hawk, Gray Hawk

ADULTS Upper parts bluish slate-gray; head blackish; a white line over and behind the eye. Inner tail feathers similar in color to the back, the outer ones brownish and lightly marked with blackish. Tip of tail whitish. Under parts entirely and finely marked with irregular wavy lines and bars of gray and white. Throat and upper breast slightly streaked with blackish.

YOUNG Upper parts dark brown, the feathers margined with reddish-brown. Primaries barred with black. Tail brownish-gray, barred with black. Under parts white or whitish, streaked with black.

BODY LENGTH	*WINGSPREAD*
Male, 20 to 22 inches	Male, 44 to 44½ inches
Female, 22 to 26½ inches	Female, 44 to 47 inches

The Goshawk, most savage, fleet, powerful, and fearless, is one of the rarest of the northeastern birds of prey. No one has described its attributes better than Edward Howe Forbush: "Among all fierce raptores that inhabit the continent of North America there is no hawk handsomer than the Goshawk. Its attack is swift, furious, and

15

deadly. In the death grapple it clings ferociously to its victim, careless of its own safety, until the unfortunate creature succumbs to its steely grip. Its stroke is terrible. It is delivered with such force as sometimes to tear out most of one side of its victim, and its wing power is so great that it can carry off rabbits and full-grown fowls."

The light bluish-gray hue of this fine dashing bird, its swift, impetuous, and yet perfectly controlled flight—making our most spectacular airplane antics appear like unskillful and lubberly performances—these combined with the creature's rarity make it one of the most attractive subjects of study by students of the out-of-doors. No one can watch the maneuvers of a Goshawk in its hunting without a thrill of pleasure. The bird pursues its agitated prey through the air with bewildering rapidity, the hawk turning, dropping, rising, following every twist and turn exactly in the wake of its fleeing quarry. The chase is of short duration, for no bird can hope to outmaneuver this combination of thunderbolt and dive bomber. It is, I believe, the most fearless of any of our birds of prey. Numerous instances are told of its daring. In northern Massachusetts I was unable to drive one out of a small grove of white pines; the bird sailed out a short distance with a defiant *keck, keck* and then returned almost to the same spot, from which I had with difficulty driven it with sticks and stones only a minute or so before. No instance of the bird's temerity, however, is more startling than the one reported by Dr. A. K. Fisher which occurred near East Windsor Hill, Connecticut: "A Goshawk flew after a fowl near a dwelling house; the door being open the hen flew inside; the hawk followed and seized her in a room occupied by an old gentleman and his daughter." At another time, reports Dr. Fisher, a farmer caught a fowl, took it to the chopping block, severed its neck, and threw it on the ground. In an instant a Goshawk which had been watching the procedure swooped, seized the still struggling body, and bearing it off not farther than ten rods or so began tearing and devouring it.

The Goshawk is not much given to vocalization. The only notes I have ever heard the bird utter are the usual harsh, abrupt *cack,*

17

cack, cack sounds, sometimes rising in pitch so as more closely to resemble the syllables *keck, keck, keck.* Its screaming notes, *kee-yee, kee-yee,* or *ki-yeear, ki-yeear,* seem to be reserved for those occasions on which the nest is being attacked and when the birds are themselves attacking the intruders, or during the mating season. Jacob Bates Abbott, who studied the nesting of the Goshawk at Mt. Monadnock in southern New Hampshire in 1941 relates that ". . . when we were within two hundred yards of the site [of the nest] the shrill *keee-yr* of the Goshawks rang through the woods. The . . . . bird swooped low through the trees several times . . . and screamed insistently . . . At no time did either hawk come closer than seventy-five feet, although they screamed persistently, a shrill *keee-y,* or *keee-yr,* with very little of the cackle or *cac-cac-cac* so often used to describe the Goshawk's scream."

The Goshawk's breeding range is chiefly in Canada, but the bird breeds very sparingly in the high mountains of Vermont, New Hampshire, Massachusetts, and New York, and southward in decreasing numbers along the crests of the Alleghenies. In northern New England and New York it is a very rare summer resident and irregular winter visitant. In central New England it is fairly common in winter, but it seldom visits southern New England. In New Jersey it is to be found almost entirely in the northwestern and western portions among the high wooded hills as an irregular straggler during the winter months except when unusually severe winters drive it farther to the southward.

The birds breed in deep forests, particularly in wild mountain regions, placing their bulky and rather ill-formed nests of sticks lined with the twigs of conifers, weed stalks, bits of bark, and the like well up in a tall tree, usually an evergreen. The nest on Mount Monadnock studied by Jacob Bates Abbott was thirty-eight feet from the ground in the triple crotch of a white pine, at an elevation of about sixteen hundred feet.

The Goshawk is the palest gray of any of our native hawks (except the Marsh Hawk in the "light phase" of its plumage) with silvery, whitish-gray under parts. When in flight its wings appear short and somewhat rounded in contrast to those of the Marsh Hawk, which appear longer and more slender. The flight of the Goshawk somewhat resembles that of the Cooper's Hawk; a series of short glides alternates with periods of rapid, vigorous flapping, accompanied by occasional impetuous dashes into thickets and groves, and is quite different from the leisurely glides and rather languid flapping exhibited by the Marsh Hawk as it gracefully follows the undulations of moor and meadow. The immature Goshawks, brownish above and prominently streaked below, are almost exact counterparts of immature Cooper's Hawks except that a large female Goshawk would be larger than the average female Cooper's Hawk.

Poultry, ducks, grouse, other game birds, and many species of small birds constitute the greater part of the food of this rapacious hawk. It must be noted, however, that much of its food is made up of such agriculturally noxious creatures as rabbits, mice, rats, and other small mammals and insects, so that even though the hawk takes some toll among birds, it is not wholly detrimental.

5

Sharp-Shinned Hawk

~~~~~~

ACCIPITER STRIATUS VELOX

ALSO CALLED

Little Blue Darter, Pigeon Hawk, Bullet Hawk,
Bird Hawk, Partridge Hawk, Chicken Hawk,
Slate-Colored Hawk, Fowl Hawk

ADULTS Upper parts slate gray, primaries barred with black-ish. Tail ashy gray crossed with blackish bars; tip whitish and al-most square across. Throat white with blackish streaks; the rest of the under parts barred with white and light reddish-brown.

YOUNG Upper parts dark brown, the feathers margined with reddish brown. Primaries and tail similar to those of the adults. Under parts white or whitish, streaked or spotted with blackish or pale reddish-brown.

BODY LENGTH	*WINGSPREAD*
Male, 10 to 12 inches	Male, 20 to 23 inches
Female, 12 to 14 inches	Female, 24 to 27 inches

"Thar goes a blue darter—ye mean littil cuss—but yer smart, an' quicker 'n lightnin'." Thus an old Maine woodsman friend of mine apostrophized a Sharp-Shinned Hawk that had dashed across a woodland glade not ten feet from where we were standing, in hot pursuit of a terror-stricken sapsucker whose frantic zig-zags finally landed it safe among the thick bristling branches of a dead spruce.

20

One often sees this little hawk, though "quicker 'n lightnin'," miss its quarry thus, a circumstance which impresses anew upon the mind of the thoughtful observer the fact that it is usually only the weaker birds whose powers of flight are impaired that fall victim to birds of prey.

Our little Sharp-Shinned Hawk is one of the most agile of hunters. It does not sit patiently watching for its prey as do the Red-Tailed and Broad-Winged Hawks, but is continually on the wing. If its intended meal happens to be a smaller bird in full flight, it dashes after it at top speed, following every twist and turn of the quarry, until suddenly it reaches out with its long curved talons and snatches the bird out of mid-air without even checking its own flight. The Sharp-Shinned Hawk may be encountered in any sort of country—though it is most often seen in the neighborhood of moderately wooded areas, farm lands, bushy pastures, and hillsides grown up with saplings—beating back and forth low over the tops of the trees and low bushes or sailing and flapping straight ahead, never very high. A Sharp-Shinned Hawk will often dash headlong into a bush in close proximity to an observer with apparent fearlessness, scattering a flock of small birds like leaves before a high wind and usually emerging with some luckless songster in its talons. Invariably the watcher's sympathies go with the smaller bird—one seldom reflects on the hawk's need of food, or rejoices because it has found something to allay its pangs of hunger.

Occasionally the Sharp-Shin attacks birds much larger and heavier than itself, sometimes even striking a quarry so heavy that the hawk is unable to lift it. In such a case pieces of the flesh are stripped off and swallowed on the spot. Quail are sometimes struck, as well as young pheasants, chickens, and grouse, but these larger birds are not the usual food of the hawk, smaller birds being much more to its taste. More than seven-eighths of its food consists of the smaller species of birds, that is, birds smaller than a Robin or a Blue Jay. Sharp-shins may become a great local pest when a pair elect to make their nest near some farm where young chickens can be readily procured. Mice form a small proportion of their dietary, and some larger insects such as grasshoppers, crickets, and large beetles are also eaten. In the wilderness and under natural conditions the bird should by no means be disturbed. Here it is entirely beneficial, forming one of nature's indispensable checks upon the undue increase of unsound individuals among the smaller birds.

The shrill cries of the Sharp-Shinned Hawk, less loud than those of its congener the Cooper's Hawk, sound somewhat like the prolonged squealing *peeeeek* of the Hairy Woodpecker and are raised in menacing alarm whenever the locality of the nest is invaded. Another call like the syllables *cac, cac, cac* is frequently uttered, but the bird is by no means a noisy one.

Against the main stem of trees and from twenty to eighty feet above the ground the Sharp-Shinned Hawk builds its bulky nest, a structure composed of sticks, very cleverly and neatly interlaced, with a relatively deep central cavity lined with smaller twigs, strips of bark, leaves, grass, and weed stems, and sometimes with bits of paper, mosses, dried fern fronds, or a few feathers. The bird is in general a forest-nester; nevertheless one may sometimes find its nest in open woodlands or small grooves, in either coniferous or deciduous trees, and usually well concealed from below. Occasionally the deserted nest of a squirrel, crow, or another hawk may be used as a foundation, and I once found a nest which appeared to have been erected upon the unusually large loose platform of a Mourning Dove. There are usually from four to five eggs, but infrequently six or even eight are found. They are a soiled white or white tinged with faint hues of blue or green, blotched and spotted with various shades and tints of brown, lavender, or lilac. These markings vary greatly.

During the last weeks of April and the first weeks of May, Sharp-Shinned Hawks by the hundreds and thousands wing their way northward through the northeastern states, riding high on the air currents that sweep upward from the sides of the extended mountain ridges of the Appalachians, and pass northward up the Connecticut and Hudson River Valleys along the flanks of the Berkshires and the lesser mountains and hills of southern New England, through the great valleys of the White and Green Mountains—sailing, flapping, mile after mile, and sometimes in a burst of spirits engaging in aërial battles with one another or rising higher and higher in the blue in a series of wide and soaring sweeps.

Most of these attractive little hawks breed in Canada, but some breed in Maine, New Hampshire, northern New York, and Vermont, and less frequently in the mountains southward. Throughout New Jersey and Pennsylvania the bird is found as a very common migrant in spring and fall. During the great hawk migrations along the central mountain ridges as well as at Cape May, New Jersey, it is one of the most abundant species. During the fall of 1935, for example, at Cape May Mr. William Rusling counted 8,206 Sharp-Shins, as against only 840 Cooper's Hawks (their nearest relatives) and only 2,706 of all other species of hawk combined. In September, October, and November of 1941, Mr. Maurice Broun at Hawk Mountain, Drehersville, Pennsylvania, observed 3,909 Sharp-Shins as against 416 Cooper's and 11,564 of all other species. Sharp-Shinned Hawks rarely winter in northern New England or New York, but increase in numbers southwards into New Jersey.

The Sharp-Shinned Hawk may sometimes be identified in flight by its small size (it is only slightly larger than the Sparrow Hawk and often not even so large as the familiar Blue Jay). Its short, rounded wings and narrow, square-tipped tail serve to distinguish it from the Cooper's Hawk when the difference in the size of the two species is not apparent. The female Sharp-Shinned, being larger than the male, is almost as large as a small male Cooper's.

24

6
Cooper's Hawk

~~~~~~

ACCIPITER COOPERII

ALSO CALLED

Big Blue Darter, Chicken Hawk, Hen Hawk, Big Bullet Hawk, Black-Capped Hawk, Quail Hawk, Partridge Hawk, Pigeon Hawk, Long-Tailed Hen Hawk, Swift Hawk, Blue Hawk

ADULTS Similar to the Sharp-Shinned Hawk, but larger and bearing a blackish crown patch. End of tail rounded when seen in flight instead of square-cut as in the Sharp-Shinned species.

YOUNG Similar in coloration to the young of the Sharp-Shinned Hawk.

BODY LENGTH
Male, 14 to 18 inches
Female, 16½ to 20 inches

WINGSPREAD
Male, 27 to 30 inches
Female, 29 to 36 inches

"Cooper's Hawk is a forest rover. It is cradled in wind-swept woods, and fledged amid the creaking and groaning of great trees. Alert, swift, and dauntless, it roams the greenwood with falcon-like freedom, carrying terror to the hearts of weaker creatures, and leaving behind it a trail of destruction and death. When the Cooper's loud 'cucks' ring through the sunny leafy woods of June, the hush of death pervades everything. All erstwhile cheerful thrushes and warblers become still and silent. The Cooper's fierce 'cucks' are the

25

most merciless sounds of our summer woods. There is indeed death in the air!" (Edward Howe Forbush.)

From the exhaustive studies which have been made there is little doubt that the Cooper's Hawk more than any other species is responsible for the ill repute in which all hawks are held by the farmer. No other hawk is so pre-eminently a "chicken hawk." Whatever has been said concerning the Sharp-Shinned Hawk applies in greater measure here. Because of the larger size of the Cooper's Hawk, however, it is more destructive to poultry and game birds than its smaller congener. Small birds form only about one-half its food, and poultry and game birds more than a quarter. It takes few insects and but few injurious rodents, though when birds are scarce these make up a much greater proportion of its dietary. But feathered prey is much more to its taste. Its powers of talon and of wing are surprising. It does not scruple to seize birds almost as large and as heavy as itself and with laborious flapping will often bear off a half-grown fowl. I have seen it strike its talons into a full-grown hen which it was unable to raise from the ground. When attacked, the hawk actually showed fight before it relinquished its grasp and flew away. Its courage entitles it to respect. Perhaps as a remedial measure, it will occasionally include some vegetable material in its diet. Thus the stomach of an immature female bird which I examined one November contained, besides the remains of two Juncos and a Meadow Mouse, a large mass of coarse vegetable fibre similar under the microscope to the bark of goldenrod or aster stems.

Cooper's and Sharp-Shinned Hawks are alike in color, and almost exactly so in contour. But the tail of the Cooper's is rounded at its tip, whereas the tail of the Sharp-Shin is cut squarely across, a distinction which is easily recognizable in the field. Since male hawks are smaller than females, a small male Cooper's would be almost the same size as a large female Sharp-Shin. In such cases the shape of the tail is of the greatest value for identification.

The Cooper's Hawk indulges in more sailing and less flapping than does the Sharp-Shinned Hawk, and its wing beats are not so rapid. Moreover, it often flies at higher altitudes. But like the Sharp-Shin it makes its way through the air in alternate periods of gliding and flapping. When hunting it dashes rapidly, now near the ground, now just skimming the tops of the trees and bushes, or weaves its way with astonishing rapidity and dexterity between tree trunks and thickly interlaced branches as it pursues at top speed some warbler or finch. The impetuosity of its rush after its prey often precipitates the bird into the very midst of a dense coppice or briar tangle which may give it considerable difficulty in emerging.

Although this much maligned hawk is stigmatized as malicious, cruel, and detrimental and though it is relegated to the ranks of "vermin," yet the fact remains that it is a strong, daring, courageous, splendid bird of prey—perfect of its kind. To students of biology it is seen to be one of nature's most effective regulators of avine eugenics. It should never be molested or shot in its native haunts.

Cooper's Hawks nest in forests, moderately wooded lands, and sometimes in groves of coniferous or deciduous trees. Often the top of a white pine is chosen as the nesting site. The nest itself, from twenty-five to seventy-five feet or so from the ground, is composed of sticks well interlaced, and is lined with strips of bark and twigs, not infrequently with a mixture of large weed stems, leaves, or bits of moss and coarse grasses. A deserted nest is sometimes used as a foundation.

The eggs, from two to six in number, are sub-oval, often almost spherical. They are either an unmarked whitish, or else tinged with bluish or greenish hues and faintly spotted with brown, lilac, or some similar tint, the spots sometimes being arranged in a rough band near the larger end of the egg.

Although the Cooper's Hawk breeds chiefly north of our borders, it may be found breeding in northern New England and New York and to a less extent farther southward into the hills of northern and western New Jersey, its numbers decreasing southwards. In the spring and fall it occurs as a fairly common migrant along the mountain ridges of the Middle Atlantic States.

7

Eastern Red-Tailed Hawk

wwwwwwwwwwwwwwwwwwwwwwwwwwwwwwwwwwwwwwwwwww

BUTEO JAMAICENSIS BOREALIS

ALSO CALLED

Red Hawk, Chicken Hawk, Hen Hawk,
Red-Tailed Buzzard, Squealing Hawk,
Buzzard Hawk, White-Breasted Chicken
Hawk, White-Breasted Buzzard

ADULTS Upper parts dark grayish or fuscous brown, the feathers irregularly edged with shades of reddish brown, buff, and white. Upper surface of tail rich reddish-brown. Upper breast streaked with grayish-brown and buff; lower breast lightly streaked or not at all. Upper abdomen lightly streaked, spotted, or barred with black or blackish, the markings often forming a sort of broken, indefinite band. Lower abdomen usually white and unmarked.

YOUNG Similar, but lacking the red tail, which is generally about the same color as the back and is crossed by many blackish bars. There is no brownish in the markings of the under parts.

BODY LENGTH	*WINGSPREAD*
Male, 19 to 22 inches	Male, 46 to 50 inches
Female, 21 to 25 inches	Female, 48 to 56 inches

Few of our native birds are more misunderstood or are more maligned in popular terminology than this majestic species of native hawk. The terms "chicken hawk" and "hen hawk," often applied to

it, are entire misnomers. An examination of more than 560 stomachs (made by our Federal Fish and Wildlife Service) has shown that not more than 10 percent of the food consists of poultry and game birds, whereas 85 percent consists of injurious rodents, principally Meadow Mice and their kin. The bird might be more fittingly called the mouse hawk. During the winter months the Red-Tail consumes thousands upon thousands of Meadow or Field Mice (*Microtus*), at once the most destructive rodent and the most numerous mammal on our continent. During the summer it feeds not only upon these creatures, but also upon rabbits (also notably destructive), as well as upon rats, squirrels, shrews, and other small mammals. It consumes uncountable thousands of grasshoppers (locusts), and other large noxious insects. When pressed by extreme hunger in hard winters, some individuals will take poultry and game birds and some small song birds. At such times it strikes and devours skunks, and does not disdain even carrion and offal.

The Red-Tailed Hawk is to be numbered among our most regal birds. It contributes much to the beauty and interest of our landscapes. With widely expanded wings it may be seen sailing overhead in ever widening circles, higher and higher, until, becoming a mere speck in the blue, it finally passes from sight. Its powers of sustained flight are astonishing. A competent observer states that one of these tireless hawks was observed to soar continually without once alighting from seven o'clock in the morning until four o'clock in the afternoon!

During these periods of sailing and soaring the bird is not hunting, as many believe. When in need of food the Red-Tailed Hawk does not soar but sits. Motionless, except for a slow movement of the head bearing the ever-watchful eyes, it perches upon a dead limb or elevated crag or some similar coign of observation, watching for its quarry to come within range. Then suddenly it dashes down and strikes.

The Red-Tail is usually seen as a soaring hawk. As it wheels through the air in the completion of one of its great circles, the sidewise tilting of its widely spread, fan-shaped tail will at some point in the circuit bring its upper surface momentarily into view even if the bird is at a considerable elevation. At such times a watcher from below who has field glasses will have no difficulty in distinguishing its rich, reddish-brown color. This will identify the adult bird. It is the only one of our northeastern soaring hawks which shows no barrings on the tail while in flight, since the narrow blackish zone near the tip of the tail and its terminal white band are not perceptible at any great distance. Sometimes the bright sunlight falling through the tail will reveal its reddish-brown cast, though this color is not so pronounced as that reflected from the upper surface of the feathers.

The tail of the immature bird is a grayish brown, crossed by many blackish bars.

The wing strokes of the Red-Tailed Hawk are less frequent and more labored than those of the other buteonine hawks (the Red-Shouldered Hawk and the Broad-Winged Hawk) with which the bird might be confused. Moreover its periods of sailing on set pinions are longer, and the widths of its soaring spirals are greater.

In the spring of the year the cheerful scream of the Red-Tailed Hawk is one of the characteristic and pleasing sounds of the countryside. As the bird wheels high in the air, it emits a far-reaching and long-drawn *kee-eeaarr, kee-eeaarr,* a note which in ringing quality of tone and exhilaration of spirit is reminiscent of that other loud and jubilant utterance of a crisp spring morning, the song of the Meadowlark. About the vicinity of the nest the parent birds utter a variety of notes, one sounding like a suppression of the soaring scream, *kit-chee, kit-chee,* another an abrupt piercing scream or squeal, *kirrr,* and a series of low, conversational notes like the syllables *churr, churr, churr.*

In the far north Red-Tailed Hawks' nests are commonly to be found in coniferous trees, but in the southern part of their range, deciduous trees seem to be the usual site. They are frequently very bulky structures, for the same pair of birds may return to the same nest year after year, adding fresh material each spring. When the leaves are off the trees the nests are conspicuous objects since they are placed at a considerable elevation, from twenty-five feet up to as high as the branches will support the heavy structures. They are composed of large sticks and smaller twigs, sometimes unlined, sometimes lined with weed stalks, dried leaves, bits of bark, corn husks, twigs of pine, spruce, hemlock, or other trees, often with bunches of the fresh leaves attached, and in one case, with many fragments of tough brown paper.

Both sexes assist in the building of the nest and in the incubation of the eggs of which there are usually from two to four, the smaller number prevailing. The eggs are white or light in hue, faintly tinted with yellowish or bluish, frequently unmarked, but sometimes blotched or spotted with reddish-brown, yellowish-brown, gray, or lilac, in various depths of intensity.

The Red-Tailed Hawks are fairly common in the Northeast as migrating individuals in the spring and fall. They breed in some numbers among the hills and mountains, but are found only rarely along the coastal zones. In winter one may come across Red-Tailed Hawks almost anywhere except in the most northerly parts of New York, Vermont, New Hampshire, and Maine, though at this season they cannot be called common anywhere. As one travels southward in winter, he encounters them in greater numbers, especially in the southern portion of New Jersey where in some winters they have been quite common.

8

Northern Red-Shouldered Hawk

∿∿

BUTEO LINEATUS LINEATUS

ALSO CALLED

Winter Hawk, Winter Falcon, Singing Hawk, Hen Hawk, Chicken Hawk, Red-Shouldered Buzzard

ADULTS Upper parts rich, dark reddish-brown, the feathers more or less edged with darker grayish-brown, yellowish-brown, and white. Four outer primaries barred with black and white; shoulder patch reddish-brown. Tail black or dark grayish-brown, with four or five white crossbars and a white tip. Under parts brown or grayish-brown, everywhere barred with white and light gray. Throat streaked with blackish.

YOUNG Similar to the adults, but the tail grayish-brown, indistinctly barred with blackish. Under parts white or whitish, streaked or spotted with black.

BODY LENGTH	WINGSPREAD
Male, 18 to 23 inches	Male, $32\frac{1}{2}$ to 44 inches
Female, 19 to 24 inches	Female, $39\frac{1}{8}$ to 50 inches

From out the azure depths of the sky on a quiet June day comes the faint, musical scream of the Red-Shouldered Hawk, *kee-yeeaar, kee-yeeaarr*. It is one of the most agreeable notes uttered by any of our native birds of prey, as one of its local names, Singing Hawk, testifies. Its call reminds one of the call of the Blue Jay, although

34

the hawk's note is clear and pure and lacks the Jay's discordant and peevish quality. This clarity of tone also serves to distinguish the call from the somewhat similar but harsher notes of its larger congener, the Red-Tailed Hawk. Other notes of the Red-Shouldered Hawk, uttered when the bird is disturbed or angered, sound like the screamed syllables *kee-yeck, kee-yeck,* with a frequently interjected, rapid *keck, keck, keck,* all given with a harsh vigor, unlike the rather leisurely *kee-yeeaarr* note. Besides these utterances, there are several soft, subdued, clucking notes, like those of a mother hen, when the parent birds are engaged in their many ministrations about the nest.

It is in low, wooded country, where open fields, meadows, swamps, and streams abound, that one must look for the Red-Shouldered Hawks. Unlike their larger red-tailed relatives the birds do not retreat before man's occupation of the land, but continue their residence and their hunting, even in farming districts, as long as sufficiently numerous groves of tall trees remain to afford lodgment for their nests. They are seldom found in heavily forested regions, or among high hills, or in mountainous, rocky terrain. Thus in the Adirondacks, the Green Mountains, the White Mountains, the Berkshires, and the hills of northern New Jersey one sees them only rarely except where low marshes lie along stream valleys. During the spring and fall migrations, they appear in groups or singly, coasting along some extended mountain ridge or drifting high in the air.

In their habit of soaring in great spirals on fixed wings, they resemble the Red-Tailed and the Broad-Winged Hawks. They are like these hawks in their hunting also; perched upon a stump or dead limb not far from the ground they remain motionless for long intervals watching for passing quarry. At such times they may be quite closely approached before they take flight.

Field mice and other small mammals such as shrews, young rabbits, squirrels, and moles, or amphibians like frogs and toads, and large insects form the chief food of this so-called hen hawk. Small birds are seldom taken, and poultry and game birds still more infrequently. Other items in the dietary are fish, crayfish, spiders and the like, and snakes. These last seem to be a favorite food with the Red-Shoulder. I have repeatedly seen the birds flying with snakes clutched in their talons twice the length of their captors. The diet of this species is more varied than that of any other of our birds of prey. Since it destroys so many mice, other injurious small mammals, and insects, it seems hardly necessary to point out that the bird deserves protection and encouragement in breeding.

In its form and structural materials, the nest of the Red-Shouldered Hawk is generally similar to that of the Red-Tailed Hawk, but smaller and not so high. One nest which I examined contained a large quantity of bark fragments about the size of the bowl of a tablespoon. Watching the birds through a mounted telescope nearly a quarter of a mile away, I concluded from the motions of the parents' heads and from the quantity of feathers found subsequently in the nest, that the parents added feathers from their own breasts to this harsh lining.

Parent hawks defend their nest valiantly, swooping at the intruder and screaming continuously. From two to six eggs are laid, typical of the hawks in their coloration, white, creamy, pale or spotted blue, or splotched with brown, gray, pink, and lilac.

Red-shouldered Hawks in flight and in any plumage may be distinguished from all our other native hawks by a whitish or seemingly translucent patch near the tip of the wing, just beyond the bend of the wing (in reality the wrist of the bird). Four or five narrow white bars on the tail showing in flight offer a convenient field mark for separating this species from the Broad-Winged and Swainson's Hawks, in which the white barrings are fewer and appreciably broader, and from the Red-Tailed Hawk, which shows no bars on the tail.

Red-Shouldered Hawks breed all summer in the Northeast except in high hills and mountains, dense forests, or along the coast. After the Sparrow Hawk they are the commonest bird of prey. Very

sides as far as trees will grow. It often soars to great heights on its ample wings after the manner of its congeners, the Red-Tailed and Red-Shouldered Hawks. I once watched a Broad-Winged Hawk with a 50-power telescope from the altitude of 2,100 feet on Mount Monadnock in southern New Hampshire. It rose above a woodland in the valley below and gradually spiraled upward until it became a mere dot in the blue. Its altitude was estimated at more than 7,000 feet.

The voice of the Broad-Winged Hawk is in keeping with its gentle disposition and pacific habits, being a mild, almost plaintive note, too subdued to be called a scream, but sounding more like a much magnified call of the Wood Pewee. It may be represented by the syllables *pwee-teee,* or *ki-weee.* When the nest is approached, the parent birds fly about without apparent concern, uttering a somewhat harsh but subdued and querulous *cac, cac, cac.*

Broad-Winged Hawks place their nest high up in a tree, usually close to the main trunk from twenty-five to fifty feet from the ground. Sticks and twigs compose its outer structure; within is a lining of bits of bark, mosses, lichens, dry grasses, and small weed stems, sometimes leaves, and occasionally a few feathers. The whole structure is often built up on the foundation of an abandoned crow's or hawk's nest; sometimes the great amount of dried leaves under the nest suggests that a deserted Gray Squirrel's nest was used as a foundation. Like other hawks, the Broad-Wing may return year after year to the same nest.

The eggs number from two to four and vary greatly in color and markings. They are white, creamy, or flushed with bluish, pinkish, or greenish; sometimes they are plain and unmarked, at other times variously spotted, blotched, scrawled, or lined with many shades of brown, gray, lavender, and similar colors. These markings are usually clustered more heavily about the larger end.

Every effort should be made to protect this valuable bird and encourage its multiplication. With a dietary almost three-quarters of which is composed of insects and mice and other rodents, it is a friend of farmers, not a foe. It seldom molests small birds. Reptiles, frogs, toads, and salamanders form an important item of its food. One service which it performs deserves special mention, that of destroying immense numbers of the very injurious larvae of large moths.

Of our four common buteonine hawks—Red-Tailed Hawk, Red-Shouldered Hawk, Rough-Legged Hawk, and Broad-Winged Hawk —the last named is the smallest. Its wingspread is about equal to that of the Common Crow, although the breadth of its wings makes it appear larger in the air.

The Broad-Winged Hawk is not likely to be confused with any other species except the Red-Tailed and the Red-Shouldered Hawks. The adult Broad-Wing may be distinguished from the adult Red-Tail in flight by the barrings on its tail, which the Red-Tail lacks. The number and width of these barrings distinguish it from the adult Red-Shoulder. The Broad-Winged Hawk shows two to four *wide* white bands on a dark ground, whereas the Red-Shouldered Hawk shows five or six *narrow* white bands.

Young Broad-Winged Hawks are unlike young Red-Tails in that their under parts are uniformly dark-streaked, the under parts of the Red-Tails being white divided about midway by a bellyband of dark streaks. They may be distinguished from young Red-Shoulders only with difficulty, since young Broad-Wings exhibit tails with several narrow whitish bands similar to those of the Red-Shoulders. In general, Broad-Winged Hawks show shorter, wider wings and tail.

The Rough-Legged Hawk (in its normal or light plumage) has a black patch at the bend of the wing which prevents the observer from confusing it with the Broad-Wing, which does not have it.

Broad-Winged Hawks are more stocky than Red-Shouldered, Red-Tailed, or Rough-Legged Hawks. They are slightly smaller than the Red-Shouldered species, and appreciably smaller than the Red-Tailed and Rough-Legged. These differences are useful criteria for recognition when the birds are seen in the air at the same time or in rapid succession, their use depending, of course, on the accuracy of the visual memory of the observer.

The Broad-Winged Hawk is a common spring and fall migrant throughout the Northeast and commonly breeds in summer wherever there are broad woodlands except in New York and in western and central Vermont. In this latter state it is also rare or absent as a migrant. In the Adirondacks it is said to be the commonest of all the hawks. It does not often breed in Rhode Island or Connecticut. Most of the Broad-Wings leave the area completely during the fall, but occasionally a few individuals may winter along the southern Connecticut shore and the tip of southern New Jersey.

10

Swainson's Hawk

~~~~~~

BUTEO SWAINSONI

ALSO CALLED

Grasshopper Hawk, Hen Hawk, Chicken Hawk,
Gopher Hawk, Prairie Hawk, Prairie Buzzard,
Brown Hawk, Black Hawk

ADULTS In normal, or light phase: Upper parts dark grayish-brown; edges of feathers light yellowish-brown; forehead light. Tail with many narrow faint whitish bars and a narrow whitish tip. Upper breast light or dark reddish-brown. Rest of under parts white or pale flesh color barred with brownish, especially on the sides. Chin and throat, white.

In dark phase: Entire bird mantled with dusky brown; flanks lighter barred with blackish-brown. Under tail coverts white with dusky spots. Forehead and chin whitish, sometimes streaked. Birds may display all gradations between light and dark phases.

YOUNG In normal, or light phase: Upper parts blackish-brown, marked with yellowish-brown. Head and under parts light, fawn color, streaked with blackish-brown, and spotted on sides with the same color.

In dark phase: Plumage everywhere darkened by dusky brown.

BODY LENGTH	WINGSPREAD
Male, 18¾ to 20½ inches	Male, 47¼ to 51 inches
Female, 18⅞ to 22 inches	Female, 47 to 57 inches

44

The name Swainson's Hawk memorializes William Swainson, the English naturalist, who together with that famous traveler and observer Sir John Richardson published the *Fauna Boreali-Americana* in 1837. The stately Swainson's Hawk is not, strictly speaking, an eastern species. It occurs in large numbers in the West, is found but rarely east of the Mississippi, and reaches the northeastern states only as a very infrequent straggler. But since Swainson's Hawks in their dark-plumage phases are difficult to identify in the field, it is conceivable that the species may be more numerously represented than is generally believed.

Like the Red-Shouldered Hawk, the Swainson's Hawk is a bird of partially wooded country or even prairie lands, as its alternate name Prairie Hawk implies. My only experience with this hawk was during a winter in Mississippi and Oklahoma, where it seemed to be an unusually silent species, giving voice only occasionally to a subdued screaming note, *kreee, kreee*. It is said to produce a peculiar gurgling sound while in flight and a repeated note like the syllables *pi-tick, pi-tick*.

The nest of the Swainson's Hawk is in general similar to that of the Red-Shouldered Hawk in location and structure, being the usual "bushel basket of sticks" lined with weed stalks, coarse grasses, and leaves. Unlike the Red-Shouldered Hawk, however, the Swainson's sometimes places the nest low down on a cliff ledge, low tree or bush, or even upon the ground. It lays from two to four eggs. They are almost white but are sometimes very heavily marked, sometimes finely speckled and scrawled, but more often only moderately spotted and blotched with various shades of brown, purplish-gray, and lavender.

Swainson's Hawk is a typical Buteo, with the tail held fan-shaped while in flight. It possesses somewhat longer and narrower wings than its congeners the Red-Tailed, Red-Shouldered, and Broad-Winged Hawks. In the light phase of its plumage it most closely resembles the Red-Tailed Hawk, but its wings are not so broad, and it exhibits a dark upper breast which forms a sort of

46

wide band separating the whitish throat from the light-colored abdomen. Young individuals in the light-plumage phase closely resemble the young of both Red-Tails and Red-Shoulders. In the dark-plumage phase, which is the more common one in the northeast and the one shown in our illustration, the species is difficult to identify either as an adult or as an immature bird.

The diet of the Swainson's Hawk is extremely varied. It consists more of insects than that of any other buteonine hawk. Grasshoppers and crickets predominate in its menu, but it also devours large numbers of Meadow or Field Mice, gophers, squirrels and shrews. Rabbits, snakes, frogs, and sometimes fish are occasionally eaten. Swainson's Hawk rarely takes game birds or poultry and seldom molests the smaller song birds. In fact it is reported that not infrequently orioles swing their pendant cradles from the larger sticks projecting from their nests. Bendire says: "Compared with the majority of our hawks it is gentle and unsuspicious in disposition, living in perfect harmony with its smaller neighbors. It is no unusual sight to see other birds nesting in the same tree; and the Arkansas Kingbird goes even further than this, sometimes constructing its home under the nest of these hawks, or in the sides of it"—a statement which will remind the reader of the similar habit of grackles in nesting among the sticks of an Osprey's dwelling.

Because of its enormous consumption of destructive rodents and large insects, especially grasshoppers, all investigators agree in ranking the Swainson's Hawk as among the most useful of our native birds.

11

Rough-Legged Hawk

wwwwwwwwwwwwwwwwwwwwwwwwwwwwwwwwwwwwwwwwwwwwwwwwwwwww

BUTEO LAGOPUS SANCTI-JOHANNIS

ALSO CALLED

Black Hawk, Mouse Hawk, Hen Hawk, Squalling
Hawk, Rough-Legged Buzzard, Black-Bellied Hawk

ADULTS In normal or light phase: Upper parts dark grayish-brown, the feathers margined with whitish and light reddish-brown. Basal third (sometimes half) of tail white or whitish, the dark end having several whitish bars. Under parts vary from white to light reddish-buff, streaked, and spotted, or blotched with dark brown or black. On the abdomen these markings tend to fuse, forming a broad, irregular, blackish transverse band. Front of tarsi entirely feathered, this condition giving the bird its name.

In dark phase: Plumage dark sooty brown to almost black, the wings and tail often crossed by narrow whitish or grayish bars. Basal part of tail sometimes white or whitish.

YOUNG Similar in general to the adults, but with distal part of tail unbarred, though tipped with white. Under parts more heavily marked with black or blackish. Band across the abdomen broad and unbroken.

BODY LENGTH	*WINGSPREAD*
Male, 19½ to 22 inches	Male, 48½ to 52¼ inches
Female, 21½ to 23½ inches	Female, 52 to 56 inches

The Rough-Legged Hawk has the distinction of being the most crepuscular of all our native hawks except when migrating high in

the air, being seen most often in the evening or (less commonly) morning twilight, hunting its quarry very much after the manner of the Marsh Hawk by beating back and forth over the tops of the bushes or grass or, like the Red-Shouldered Hawk, by watching from the top of some stump or dead limb near the ground. When the bird flies below the level of the eye, its white tail patch is conspicuous. Like other buteonine hawks, the Rough-Legged Hawk may also be seen soaring high in the air, circling up and up or swinging in wide arcs high over the marshes and woods. Occasionally the bird adopts one of the procedures of the Sparrow Hawk in its search for food and hangs hovering in one spot for several minutes at a time, sometimes dropping its long feathered legs far below its body and partially extending its talons as though about to drop upon some luckless mouse or frog. Again it will hover for a few seconds, then suddenly rise several feet, hover again, then drop to its former level, repeating this sequence several times before slanting rapidly away.

The voice of the Rough-Legged Hawk sounds somewhat like the loud, high, squealing neigh of a young colt, but wilder and fiercer, and it is uttered so commonly on the hawk's breeding grounds that the bird is often called the Squalling Hawk. Its flight notes resemble the screaming syllables, *ke-ah-ke-ah, ke-yack*.

The nest of the Rough-Leg, composed of sticks and roots, is lined with weed stalks, coarse grasses, and feathers. It is a bulky structure placed near the top of a tall tree or on the ledge of a cliff overlooking a body of water. The eggs, from two to five in number, range from yellow tints to yellowish-brown and dark brown, sometimes washed or sparsely marked with gray, purple, or lavender.

In the light-colored or normal phase of its plumage the Rough-Legged Hawk may be recognized in flight by its typical buteonine shape, closely resembling the proportions of the Red-Shouldered Hawk, but the Rough-Legged Hawk is larger. Its wings and tail are longer and not so broad as those of the other Buteos. Seen from above the bird shows a broad white zone at the base of the tail, greater in area than that displayed by the Marsh Hawk. When seen from below, the prominent black patches at the bend of the wing and the blackish belly present convenient identification marks. In the dark-plumage phase the black markings on the under side of the wings extend clear to the body of the bird, broadening as they go and occupying a large part of the wing area, the remaining part being white or whitish. The base of the tail is not always white in this phase, and when it is white, the area so marked is smaller than it is during the light phase. The tail patch forms an excellent field mark when the bird flies below the level of the eye or when it turns and tilts its body sidewise when soaring overhead. At such times it resembles the Marsh Hawk, but its wings are broader, its tail is shorter, and it is altogether an appreciably heavier, less slender, and less graceful hawk. The black wing patches and dark belly can be detected by an observer even when the bird is high in the air. When soaring and circling, the Rough-Legged Hawk is less easy and assured than are the other Buteos, and the bird is apparently unable to sail for long periods without flapping.

It is unfortunate that this splendid species is not represented in the northeastern states by greater numbers, for it is the farmers' most effective ally against that constant army of aggressors, the Meadow Mice. During its winter residence with us it feeds on little else than the privates in this army. Besides Meadow Mice the Rough-Leg also preys upon such small creatures as House Mice, Deer Mice, shrews, rats, weasels, snakes, frogs, and large insects. Early prejudice was directed against this unappreciated friend of man because of its supposed attacks upon waterfowl, game birds, and poultry. Modern research has failed to find any warrant for such a supposition. Under the press of hunger many species of hawks will strike creatures not normally their fare, and probably the Rough-Leg is no exception, but ordinarily the bird will strike at nothing larger than a rat or small rabbit. The final verdict of impartial science seems to be that the Rough-Legged Hawk is our most valuable agricultural asset among birds.

Archibuteo, the chief Buteo, to give the bird its proud title, is an infrequent and irregular winter visitant in the northeastern states. Formerly it was reported commonly along the Connecticut River Valley, where it is now rare. It is found over bushy meadows and marshes, and somewhat less commonly over higher scrubby land, notably on the bushy plains in the interior of Martha's Vineyard and Cape Cod and along the southern coast of Connecticut. There are some few records from New Jersey, where the bird reaches nearly the southern limit of its range at Cape May.

12
Marsh Hawk

~~~~~~

CIRCUS CYANEUS HUDSONIUS

ALSO CALLED
Harrier, Marsh Harrier, Bog Hawk, Mouse Hawk, Blue Hawk, Frog Hawk, Snake Hawk, Rabbit Hawk, Mole Hawk, White-Rumped Hawk, White-Rumped Harrier

ADULT MALE Upper parts ashy gray, sometimes almost pearl white, sometimes tinged with brownish; upper tail coverts (rump) pure white, forming a striking field mark when the bird is in flight. Tail silvery gray, irregularly crossed by five or six black or blackish bars. Upper breast pearl gray; lower breast and abdomen white, spotted or streaked with reddish-brown.

ADULT FEMALE Upper parts brownish; head and neck streaked with light brown. The wing coverts are edged with a similar color. Upper tail coverts white, as in the male. Middle tail feathers barred with ashy gray and black, the others with yellowish-brown and black. Under parts yellowish-brown streaked with very dark grayish-brown.

YOUNG In general similar to the female, but with upper parts a trifle darker, and the under parts a dark grayish-brown. Abdomen without streaks.

BODY LENGTH	WINGSPREAD
Male, 17½ to 20 inches	Male, 40 to 45 inches
Female, 19 to 24 inches	Female, 43½ to 54 inches

53

The palm for effortless grace and buoyancy of flight should undoubtedly be awarded to the lowly Marsh Hawk. On long pliant pinions it glides tirelessly over the flat terrain of some level marsh or follows with languid and flexile wing strokes the gentle undulations of a rolling meadow or bare hillside. Its unremitting search for Meadow Mice, frogs, and similar creatures keeps it close to the ground, and rarely does it alight on any object higher than a hummock of marsh grass, haycock, large stone, fence post, or small bush. Sometimes the bird may be seen sitting partially hidden by the long grass on the summit of a low sand dune, or preening its feathers atop an old piling in the edge of a marshy lake.

It is a bird of open land, not of forests, and is rarely seen in wooded or mountainous regions except during its periods of migration. And although it is chiefly a low flier, yet it sometimes ascends to considerable altitudes, sailing in wide circles after the manner of the buteonine hawks or indulging in its astonishing acrobatics of courtship.

I once witnessed one of these courtship performances over a river valley in northern Massachusetts. Two Marsh Hawks were sailing together in small circles high in the air. Suddenly one of the birds closed its wings and plummeted headlong earthwards for perhaps a few hundred feet or more. Seen against a background darker than the sky, it presented to view the light grayish-white hue of the male bird. Then it turned at right angles and slanted upwards underneath the first bird, tumbled over and over downwards again, swooped several times toward the right and left, and completed the performance by circling rapidly upwards to join the first bird. Tranquilly sailing about each other in ever-widening circles the two birds then passed from sight.

This exhibition of pre-nuptial exuberance does not entirely drain the male's reservoir of conjugal vigor, for he still retains enough domestic ardor after the mating is a *fait accompli* to take an active part in the construction of the nest, in aiding the incubation of the eggs, and later in assisting in the care and feeding of the

55

young. Such consistently good offices are not rendered to the female by many male birds.

The nest is to be found in a marsh, low damp meadow, or less often in a field or rolling pasture land, and is placed on the ground well hidden amid a tuft of long grasses or sedges or among bushy growths. The writer once found one tucked away in the base of a mass of Groundsel bushes (*Senecio*) at the edge of a tidal marsh. It is a shallow structure composed of weed stalks and coarse grass stems with a lining of finer dry grasses. If the situation is too wet, the bird elevates the nest on a substructure of stalks and grasses, building it up a foot or more in thickness. Although one may be certain that a given tract of land harbors a pair of breeding Marsh Hawks, yet to discover the nest is a matter of no little difficulty so cleverly is the structure concealed and so furtive are the birds in their comings and goings.

The eggs, from three to five or six in number (rarely as many as seven or eight), are somewhat variable in color. Usually they are whitish, often with a faint bluish or greenish cast, generally plain, but sometimes faintly speckled, spotted, or blotched with pale hues of brown, pinkish, or lilac.

When alarmed, the Marsh Hawk screams in a high key a short *keer, keer, keer,* cackles harshly *geg, geg, geg* or *keck-eck, keck-eck, keck-eck,* or utters a high, squealing *kih, kih, kih.* All these notes are grouped in different rhythms. Other utterances include a short, weak whistle or pipe, somewhat similar to that of the Osprey, and a series of chucking and clucking notes not unlike those of domestic fowls.

Although the Marsh Hawk feeds to some extent upon young poultry or young waterfowl where these are plentiful, and may thus become a local pest, yet its very large consumption of Meadow Mice, one of the worst foes of the agriculturist, renders it a species worthy of every protection.

Poultry and game birds constitute about one-fifteenth of its diet and small birds less than a quarter. Mice, chiefly the Meadow Mouse

(*Microtus*), rats, squirrels, shrews, and other small mammals make up more than half of its food. Although its feeding habits vary somewhat with the territory and the season, in the northeastern states the species as a whole is to be regarded as decidedly beneficial. Occasionally some individuals are driven by excessive hunger to prey upon carrion, including even dead fish, or to attack prey larger than their customary fare, as when they strike rabbits or quail. There are moreover records of Marsh Hawks found feasting upon dead ducks, but all these are exceptions, not the rule.

The Marsh Hawk presents a silhouette while in flight which resembles somewhat that of the Turkey Vulture, the wings of the two birds being set at about the same angle and the tips of the primaries at the end of the wings curving upward slightly. Moreover, both birds tip and veer from side to side as they scrutinize the ground beneath. But the long, narrow, pointed wings of the Marsh Hawk, especially its long, square-tipped tail, and its habit of flying frequently below the horizon line, thus exhibiting its prominent white rump patch, make the identification of the creature an easy matter even for the tyro in bird study.

Our only other hawk bearing a white patch at the base of the tail is the Rough-Legged Hawk, but in this species the patch is much broader, the wings are shorter and more rounded at the tips, and the tail is shorter and often spread fanwise. The immature Golden Eagle bears a tail the proximal half of which is white, but even though the Marsh Hawk and the eagle might be seen together during migration, their differences in spread of wing and in length of tail would be sufficient to proclaim their identity.

The Marsh Hawk occurs in the northeast chiefly as a summer resident, but does not breed in the mountainous and densely wooded regions except in the Adirondacks, where it is found breeding among the higher lakes at altitudes from 2,000 to 3,000 feet. In winter Marsh Hawks may be found sparingly in southern New England, chiefly along the coastal zone, in the lower Hudson valley, and southward in increasing numbers. It is fairly common in winter in

57

southern New Jersey over the great marshes, particularly from Tuckerton southwards to the tip of Cape May.

A goodly number of the vast army of Marsh Hawks that travel southwards each autumn from northern New England make their way along the coastal region and may be seen during the last week of August and during September passing along the Connecticut shore of Long Island Sound, concentrated at times in the marshes, especially in the regions of Guilford, Branford, and New Haven, and later, into October, along the coastal strip of New Jersey to Cape May Point, where the most notable concentration occurs. Here several scores of them may be seen on any one favorable day wheeling over the marshes or sailing high in the air, joining with Turkey Vultures and the buteonine hawks of various species in wide gyrations—a sort of ebullition of vacation feelings following their release from the duties of nesting and rearing broods farther north. Large numbers may linger on until late in the fall if the weather is mild. As late as October 26 I have counted upwards of thirty individuals at Cape May between the morning hours of eight and twelve.

13

Osprey

〰〰〰〰〰〰〰〰〰〰〰〰〰〰〰〰〰〰〰〰〰〰〰〰〰〰〰〰〰〰〰

PANDION HALIAËTUS CAROLINENSIS

ALSO CALLED
Sea Hawk, Fish Hawk, Fish Eagle,
Fishing Eagle, Little Eagle

ADULT MALE Upper parts dark grayish-brown, the head and nape marked with white. A wide, irregular blackish stripe extends from the base of the bill backwards, encloses the eye, and passes down to merge with the dark feathers of the neck. Tail crossed by six or eight grayish, often inconspicuous, narrow bars, and narrowly tipped with white. Under parts white, the breast sometimes lightly spotted with grayish-brown.

ADULT FEMALE Similar to the male, but with the breast always spotted or streaked with grayish-brown.

YOUNG In general similar to the adults.

BODY LENGTH	*WINGSPREAD*
21 to 24½ inches	54 to 72 inches

The males and females of this species are more nearly of the same size than is the case with most hawks. Usually the hen is a trifle larger, though she may infrequently be smaller.

With a wingspread which may almost equal that of an eagle and which exceeds that of the largest of our other hawks, the Osprey

or Fish Hawk is one of the impressive sights of our summer skies. It is most commonly seen over large bodies of water, sailing or gracefully flapping, carefully scrutinizing the surface of the water beneath. Suddenly the bird checks its flight, closes its wings, and drops head-foremost into the water with a loud splash. When falling from a height, the force of its rush carries it completely beneath the waves and out of sight. In a few seconds it bursts upward from the surface with a splash larger than the one caused by its plunge and flaps quickly off toward its nest, sometimes bearing a fish in its talons. Ismaques, as the Indians call him, is not always successful in his fishing. I once watched an Osprey near East Haven, Connecticut, plunge into a small tidal estuary nine successive times without securing his fish. Upon emerging from the water after a dive, the Osprey pauses in mid-air for a wing beat or two and shakes itself after the manner of a water-soaked dog. The drops fly off, glancing in the sun like a shower of diamonds. This action may be repeated once or twice.

The Fish Hawk seizes its prey with its feet, not with its beak, and when rising and flying away turns the fish so that its head points forward, an expedient which doubtless reduces air resistance. The feet of the Osprey are especially well adapted to the bird's particular mode of hunting. They are unusually large and stout. The toes are very rough, and at the base of each talon is a large, hard, bulbous structure covered with rugose, almost spinous scales. The curved black talons themselves are uncommonly large and heavy and are remarkably sharp. The outer toe of each foot can be moved frontward or backward, like those of the owls. Each foot may therefore be transformed into a terrifying pair of rough, double-pointed pincers, the like of which does not exist among any other of our hawks. From such a clasp as these formidable engines of prehension are capable of exerting, no fish can ever escape. That such a surety of grasp is not invariably to the advantage of the bird may be inferred from the reports of several observers who note that Ospreys sometimes strike prey so large that they cannot lift it from the water. Being also unable to withdraw their talons, the birds perish by drowning. I have repeatedly seen an Osprey strike a fish so heavy that he could bear it away only by dint of the most laborious flapping. One individual which I observed apparently laboring to its utmost power of wing was carrying a fish which seemed to be a large sucker and could not have weighed more than two and a half to three pounds.

Besides the special development of the feet the Osprey shows other interesting and unique adaptations for its aquatic hunting. Its feathers are unusually heavy, tough, and oily. The singularly oleaginous character of the plumage did not escape the notice of our northern Indians. In his *History of the Mission of the United Brethren Among the Indians of North America* Loskiel says the Indians aver "that when the bird hovers over the water it possesses a power of alluring fish towards the surface by means of an oily substance contained in its body. So much is certain, that if a bait is touched with this oil, the fish bite greedily, that it appears as if it were impossible for them to resist." The head of the Osprey bears uncommonly heavy feathers, perhaps to help break the impact of the water when it plunges in headfirst. Its unusually long and muscular legs are covered as far as the heel with short feathers, but from the heel to the toe are entirely bare of feathers and covered only with heavy scales.

A variety of places may be chosen for the location of the nests. They are found in tall dead trees (the usual location), on rocky ledges of cliffs, on sand dunes or on other knolls in sight of the open sea, on the crossarms of telephone poles, on deserted buildings and towers, or on platforms erected for them on poles or housetops. The Ospreys' nests are the largest made by any of our birds of prey except the eagles, being several feet in diameter and thickness, and form prominent objects on the sky line. In building nests Ospreys show one unique trait. Before their southward migration in the fall many of them add fresh sticks to the nest as though in anticipation of the ravages which the storms of winter may make upon their domicile during their absence. The nests are composed of large and small sticks, brush, some rubbish, cornstalks, weed stalks, and the like, and are lined with softer materials such as seaweed, cedar bark, leaves, and general plant debris. The eggs, usually from two to four in number, vary greatly in shape, size, and markings. They range from white, creamy, or dusky white to a light reddish-brown blotched and spotted with varying shades of brown.

When one intrudes too near the nesting site, the parent birds fly back and forth uttering a series of sharp, high, plaintive, piping calls not unlike the loud peeping of young chickens and wholly out of proportion to such large, majestic birds. When the nest itself is attacked the cries rise in pitch, vigor, and length. Their ordinary notes, seldom uttered, are a gentle peeping and never carry very far.

The Osprey is a gentle hawk, seldom or never harming other birds and intent only on its quiet domestic duties and its quest for fish. It is a mild creature whose pacific pursuits bear out what the good Izaak Walton observed of fishing, that it is "a moderator of passions, a procurer of contentedness, and that it begat habits of peace and patience in those that professed and practiced it." So it is with the Osprey.

Other smaller birds, notably grackles, sometimes build their nests among the lower sticks of the bulky domiciles of the Osprey where the presence of the larger birds secures their homes from molestation.

The food of the Osprey consists almost wholly of fish, with an occasional water snake, frog, or salamander. The fish are chiefly species of small economic importance such as suckers, carp, sunfish, killifish, horned pouts, breams, and the like, and among the marine forms such surface-swimming species as alewives and menhaden. Dead fish are sometimes taken, and so are half-dead individuals of many species that are swimming feebly at the surface. In the vicinity of fish hatcheries the bird sometimes becomes a nuisance and as such must be dealt with as the circumstances may direct.

The fact that the Osprey does not take poultry has won for the

63

bird not only the tolerance but also the regard of the farmers. In some sections of our country poles bearing cartwheels or similar platforms have been erected to encourage the birds to nest, since their presence about the farm is a warrant that other hawks which prey on poultry will be kept at a safe distance.

Fish Hawks have no enemies. Their pacific habits, great size, strength, and formidable armament render them immune from attack except by the Bald Eagle. And even this bird makes its onslaught not with any intent to injure its smaller cousin but simply to force it to drop its captured fish, fresh fish being a delicacy which the Eagle craves but can usually secure in no other way.

There is only one species of Osprey, and it ranges over the greater part of the world. Our subspecies, the American Osprey, occurs over the entire continent of North America except along a narrow zone above the latitude of middle Hudson Bay. It breeds fairly commonly throughout our northeastern states, along the coasts, and in the neighborhood of great lakes and rivers. Rarer in the north, it becomes increasingly numerous southwards along the coasts of Massachusetts, Connecticut, Rhode Island, and Long Island, whereas in the southern part of New Jersey along the coastal zone it is so common that its great bulky nests form one of the characteristic features of nearly every horizon line. In the fall and spring migrating Ospreys may be seen sailing high overhead in almost any part of the country, though they prefer a route which follows water. At such times they are frequently mistaken for eagles. They do not as a rule pass the winter in the northeastern states.

The Osprey may be distinguished from the Bald Eagle, which most closely resembles it, by its pure white under parts; those of the eagle in any plumage are dark. Differences in size are not always apparent, but the pure white under parts are always diagnostic.

The Eagles

~~~~~~

APPROXIMATELY eighty species of eagles are now known, distributed over the entire world and embraced in the subfamilies *Milvinae, Thrasetinae, Circaetinae,* and *Aquilinae* (the true eagles to which our American species belong). The great European Lammergeier (*Gypaeius barbatus*), also frequently called the eagle, is grouped with the Old World Vultures of the subfamily *Vulturinae* and possesses structures which are considered to make it transitional between the vultures and the eagles proper. It is a magnificent bird, attaining a body length of nearly four feet and a wingspread of from nine to ten feet.

According to legend the Lammergeier was the agent of the Fates in the predestined death of the Greek poet Aeschylus. The account is thus given by Pliny in his *Natural History* (Book 10, Chapter 3) : "It is his habit to seize tortoises and break them open by dropping them from a height in the air, a circumstance which brought about the death of the poet, Aeschylus, who, with his assured belief in Heaven, was trying to avoid destruction on that day which had been foretold, as they say, by the Fates."

Aeschylus had been warned that his death would be brought about by a house falling upon his head. Each year on the fateful day he kept in the open fields. Finally a house did fall upon his head—the house of a tortoise. It may have been that the eagle in question mistook Aeschylus's bald head for a stone, and so dropped his tortoise upon it.

The earliest representation of any bird of prey is that of the eagle found engraved on tablets and seals of the kings who ruled in Sumer, on the Persian Gulf, more than four thousand years before the Christian era. After the conquest of Babylonia by the Assyrians

65

this eagle was adopted as the emblem of the conquerors. Many centuries later we find it inscribed on the royal seals of the kings of Ur of the Chaldees.

The double-headed eagle, found in the art of the Hittites of northern Syria, has been transmitted through Turkish art and still persists in various forms of European symbolism.

The Greeks regarded the eagle with great reverence as the special messenger of Jove, a reverence which was felt later by the Romans, who made the eagle the official emblem of the Republic about 87 B.C. As a silver bird on a tall standard it was borne aloft at the head of all the legions of the army. The eagle grasping Jove's thunderbolts in its claws gradually came to be regarded as the general symbol of unconquerable might (as on our own great Seal of State), and the phrase "eagles of Rome" became a common figure of speech expressing the supreme authority of the later Empire.

Charlemagne continued the use of the eagle in such a symbolism, and Napoleon in his turn placed it upon his banners. Today it is the commonest finial of most of the flagstaffs the world over except in France, where it has been replaced by the wreath.

In Christian iconography the eagle is represented as the bird of St. John the Evangelist and is depicted in sacred art bearing the Saint on its back. This may account for the use of the carved eagle with outspread wings as a support for the Scriptures on the lecterns of churches.

Anciently the eagle was regarded as the only living creature which could gaze unflinchingly into the sun. From such a habit the bird was supposed to become filled with sunlight, akin to fire itself, and thus continually to renew its youth and vigor. It is to this belief that the Psalmist alludes when he sings: "Who satisfieth thy mouth with good things, so that thy youth is renewed like the eagle's." Later it was averred that the eagle, upon the approach of old age, would plunge itself into the ocean, washing away all decrepitude, and emerge rejuvenated. Spenser refers to this tradition in the lines:

"As eagle, fresh out of the ocean wave,
   Where he hath left his plumes all hoary gray,
   And decks himself with feathers youthful, gay."

Since the eagle was looked upon as the sun bird, this periodic descent and renewed resurrection may be an allusion to the sun's setting in the western ocean and rising anew in the east in the morning.

Albertus Magnus and Aldrovandus both taught that the eagle and the osprey swam with one foot, which was webbed, and captured their food with the other, which was armed with talons. This notion persisted as late as about 1700—the time of Linnaeus. For generations men had undoubtedly seen dead eagles and ospreys, yet it seems never to have occurred to them to examine the feet. Albert the Great had said so, and that was sufficient.

Only three eagles are found in North America, the Golden Eagle (*Aquila chrysaëtos canadensis*), the Bald Eagle (*Haliaeëtus leucocephalus leucocephalus*), and the Northern Bald Eagle (*Haliaeëtus leucocephalus alascanus*). The Gray Sea Eagle (*Haliaeëtus albicilla*) has been taken only once on our continent. The Northern Bald Eagle is the largest of these. Its wingspread of from nine to ten feet exceeds that of all other birds in the northeastern states.

14

Golden Eagle

~~~~~~

AQUILA CHRYSAËTOS CANADENSIS

ALSO CALLED

*Mountain Eagle, Royal Eagle, Ring-Tailed
Eagle, Gray Eagle, Brown Eagle, Black Eagle*

ADULTS Dark brown, the feathers of the back of the head and
nape light yellowish brown. Tail faintly barred with brownish,
sometimes with a pale tip. Legs completely covered with yellowish-
brown feathers down to the base of the toes. Bill bluish-black; cere
yellowish.

YOUNG Under parts blackish-brown, upper surface of tail
whitish, with broad blackish tip.

BODY LENGTH	*WINGSPREAD*
Male, 30 to 35 inches	Male, 75 to 84 inches
Female, 35 to 41 inches	Female, 82 to 92 inches

The Golden Eagle is a bird of lonely mountain fastnesses, where
it may be seen soaring high over bare rocky ridges and peaks, steep
heavily timbered slopes, or deep valleys, often ascending to heights
far above the clouds. Unlike the Bald Eagles, which live largely
upon fish which they find dead or often secure by robbing the
patient Osprey, the Golden Eagle pursues and strikes down fairly
large prey, launching its heavy body through the air with incredible
rapidity and overtaking the swiftest fliers. Its food consists of ducks,
geese, and other waterfowl; grouse, wild turkeys, herons, and other

large birds; some smaller birds; fawns (occasionally it will attack a fairly well-grown deer); raccoons, rabbits, skunks, weasels, foxes, and other small mammals; sometimes cats, and even porcupines. Fish and even a small amount of carrion are infrequently eaten. Under the urgency of severe hunger it may also attack small pigs, lambs, calves, kids, and poultry.

Most of the old accounts of eagles attacking human beings and attempting to carry away children have very little foundation in fact. However Dr. E. H. Forbush records one instance which he says has seemed to him authentic: "I received a report from Mr. M. Semper, Mapes P.O., British Columbia, who saw the attack. Mr. Semper writes that he was at a neighbor's house sharpening a 'mower sickle' when a neighbor's little girl, Ellen Gibbs, nine years of age, came running toward the house crying, 'Mamma, there's a big chicken hawk.' At that moment said Mr. Semper, the bird sailed directly over his head in pursuit of the child. He dropped his sickle, but before he could reach her the bird had sunk its claws into her arm. He kicked the eagle, partially disabling it, when the child's mother rushed up with an axe and decapitated it. The child's arm was much discolored and cut by the grip of the bird. It was a Golden Eagle."

Golden Eagles nest high up among the mountain crags or more rarely in tall trees. The nest itself is a bulky structure composed of sticks, bark, and twigs. It is thickly lined with bark and other plant material, and may be from four to seven feet in diameter and from three to five feet in thickness.

Their usual calls are loud and shrill, the commonest one being a high, penetrating *kee, kee, kee.*

The breeding range of the Golden Eagle is interesting for its extent—the whole of the northern part of the northern hemisphere. In Europe and Asia this extends as far south as the Himalaya Mountains and into northern Africa. In the northeastern states the Golden Eagle is a rare winter visitant, appearing chiefly during the seasons of migration, though it may appear as a wanderer during other times of the year as well. It formerly bred in the mountains of Maine, the White Mountains, the Green Mountains, the northern Berkshire Hills, the Highlands of the Hudson, the Catskills, and the Adirondacks. The surprising number of Golden Eagles seen during the past few years migrating past Hawk Mountain at Drehersville, Pennsylvania, along the crests of the Allegheny Mountains, suggests that the birds are breeding much more commonly in the east than was formerly supposed. The average number of Golden Eagles seen from Hawk Mountain each season from 1934 to 1938 is 52.6 (the average number of Bald Eagles seen being 52.8). The greatest number of Golden Eagles seen in any one season was in 1937, when 73 were counted. In September, October, and November of 1941, there were recorded 55 Golden Eagles, but only 50 Bald Eagles. Immature birds have averaged about 50 percent of all individuals seen. My authority for these figures is Mr. Maurice Broun, the efficient Keeper of the Hawk Mountain Sanctuary. There are several records for the Golden Eagle even in New Jersey. Stone gives the following data on specimens secured in that State: Vineland, February 19, 1868; New Egypt, 1893; Moorestown, November 8, 1901; Crosswick's Creek, autumn of 1888; Rocky Hill, March 1881; Brown's Mills, mid-December, 1921; Cape May, October 20, 1892; and Long Branch, August 1897. L. O. Shelley, in *The Auk* for January, 1931, reports that a Golden Eagle was shot in West Chesterfield, New Hampshire, on November 14, 1930. This is said to be the first specimen taken in the state since October 9, 1899.

Adult Golden Eagles resemble immature Bald Eagles, but show a whitish region on the under side of each wing near the tip, and a white area about the base of the tail. In the *immature* Golden Eagles, which are the ones most often seen in the East, these white areas are much more extensive and pronounced. The tail of the immature bird thus appears to be white, with a broad dark terminal band. The wings of a soaring Golden Eagle appear wider and shorter than those of a Bald Eagle; the bird soars more, flaps its wings less, and ascends to greater heights than does its bald cousin.

15
Gray Sea Eagle

~~~~~~

HALIAEËTUS ALBICILLA

ALSO CALLED
*White-Tailed Eagle, White-Tailed
Sea Eagle, Great Sea Eagle, Erne*

ADULTS Entire bird dark brown; lighter grayish-brown on head and neck, and darker on the wings. Tail pure white. Bill and feet yellow.

YOUNG Entirely dark brown, including the tail. The plumage is streaked and spotted with blackish, especially on the under parts which present more of a black-streaked appearance than anywhere else. Bill black or very dark grayish; feet dull yellow.

BODY LENGTH	*WINGSPREAD*
Male, 31 to 35 inches	Male, about 84 inches
Female, 35 to 40 inches	Female, 90 to 97 inches

The Gray Sea Eagle is distributed over the northern portion of the eastern hemisphere. It formerly bred in Scotland, and still may breed in the Hebrides and the northern islands, and occurs in northern Europe, Asia, Iceland, southern Greenland, and the Aleutian Islands. In the fall it migrates south into Japan, China, northern India, southern Europe, and North Africa. It is not known to breed on our continent, but may very well do so in the far north. In its adult plumage it somewhat resembles our adult

72

Bald Eagle except for its dark head, and in its immature plumage very closely resembles the immature birds of this species. Hence it may live in North America but be overlooked, since our northernmost seacoast is not regularly patrolled at all seasons of the year by trained ornithologists.

There is one undoubted record of its occurrence on our shores, however, as far south as southeastern Massachusetts. I say "on our shores," but the fact is that we have no record that the bird ever actually touched land. A young bird was taken alive on November 14, 1914, near the Nantucket Lightship. Dr. E. H. Forbush says that, as far as is known, this was the Sea Eagle's first visit to the United States. "It might have landed on the soil of Massachusetts, but if so it probably would have reached Nantucket, if the Dutch steamer, *Arundo* had not come along past the Nantucket Light at an opportune moment to furnish a resting place for the weary bird, which was captured alive by the captain and taken to the New York Zoological Park."

My experiences with Sea Eagles may have occurred only within the walls of European museums. I say "may" because of this entry taken from my Journal of 1933: "August 16, 1933 — North Atlantic, between Southampton and New York — Today at 2 P.M. as I was sitting reading on the upper deck, I noticed a large bird sailing steadily on set wings in a southwesterly direction, high up in a patch of clear blue sky which had opened up in the low fog through which the steamer was passing at reduced speed. So great was the altitude of the bird that even with my 8x binoculars I could make out only its contour, though I *thought* I could detect a white tail. In contour and steady sailing, the bird suggested only the Bald Eagle, with which I am perfectly familiar. But could it be this species so far out at sea? Could it, by any chance, be the Sea Eagle? I like to think so! I continually adjusted the focus of the glasses, and strained my powers of vision to their utmost, but could not *unquestionably* determine a white tail. Within a few minutes the fog shut down again, blotting out both bird and sky. At this time we are roughly

900 miles south of the southern tip of Greenland, and 600 miles east of New Foundland—I should judge in about latitude 44 degrees north."

Sea Eagles breed on rocky cliffs adjacent to the ocean, or less commonly in forests near large bodies of water. Their nests are composed of sticks or sometimes masses of seaweed. The birds may return to them year after year and by addition and repair build them up into very bulky structures from six to eight feet in diameter and thickness. Two or three whitish or faintly cream-colored eggs are laid, sometimes faintly spotted with light brown and, although slightly larger, often indistinguishable from those of the Bald Eagle.

Hudson writes of the bird: "The Sea Eagle or Erne has a more varied dietary than the Golden Eagle and he hunts for his food both on the sea and on the land. In his habits he is by turns osprey, falcon, and raven. Like the osprey he drops from a considerable height onto a fish seen near the surface, and striking his talons into it, bears it away to land. But he preys more upon puffins, guillemots, and other sea-fowl than on fish. Like the Golden Eagle he destroys mountain hares, grouse, and ptarmigan, and is regarded by the shepherd as the worst enemy of the flock. But the shepherd has his revenge, for the Erne is a great lover of carrion, and may easily be poisoned. Its yelping cry is very powerful, and shriller than the scream of the Golden Eagle."

From its close relative the Bald Eagle, which it exactly resembles in habits of flight, contour, and size, the adult Sea Eagle may be distinguished by its only white member, its tail. The young of both species, however, are confusingly alike, but the general color of the immature Sea Eagle's plumage is a more uniform and lighter brown than that of the immature Bald; it is spotted above and more appreciably streaked below with blackish. The immature Bald Eagle sometimes shows whitish patches scattered about over the plumage, but these markings are absent in the plumage of the immature Sea Eagle.

75

16

Southern Bald Eagle

~~~~~~

HALIAEËTUS LEUCOCEPHALUS LEUCOCEPHALUS

ALSO CALLED

Bald Eagle, White-Tailed Eagle, White-Headed Eagle, Black Eagle, or Gray Eagle (referring to the young), Sea Eagle, Washington Eagle, Old Abe, Bird of Freedom, American Eagle, Bald-Headed Eagle

ADULTS Head, neck, and tail, pure white; rest of plumage varying from sooty brown to nearly black; tarsi partly feathered; bill and feet yellow.

YOUNG Sooty brown, varied with whitish, grayish, and blackish. Bill black.

BODY LENGTH	WINGSPREAD
Male, 30 to 34 inches	Male, 72 to 85 inches
Female, 35 to 37 inches	Female, 79 to 90 inches

The Bald Eagle was adopted as our national emblem by act of the Second Continental Congress of 1782. The spray of olive in the bird's right claw indicates the peaceful disposition of our Republic, while the bundle of arrows clutched in its left claw proclaims our ability to defend our pacific ideals.

Our national bird is not so uncommon as many suppose. When once its characteristics of contour and flight are known, the alert

observer will have no trouble in finding it in many parts of the northeastern states. The adult Bald Eagle may be distinguished from the common Osprey or Fish Hawk by its pure white head and tail, dark under parts, and wide wings. The under parts of the Osprey are pure white, its tail is dark, and its head is marked with black; its wings are appreciably narrower and more pointed. The Turkey Vulture approaches the Bald Eagle more closely in size, but the Bald Eagle in flight may be distinguished by the manner in which its wings are extended straight out from its body, forming a "straight angle" rather than forming an upward wide-open V like those of the Turkey Vulture. Moreover, the eagle's head and neck are more prominent than are the vulture's, and the larger bird is more given to sailing straight ahead, and not so much to veering, tilting, and tipping as the smaller.

The voice of the Bald Eagle is best described as a high cackling or rasping scream. A pair which once attacked me while I was photographing a nest in northern Maine swooped and wheeled about uttering a loud *screeeee-ack-ack-ack* and *screeeee-arrk, arrrk, arrrk,* varying this with a shrill *screeeeeee-iiik* and a series of *cac-cac-cac* notes similar to those uttered by many hawks. While about the nest the birds utter a series of throaty cackling notes, *carruck, carruck,* like the sounds of a hen.

The nest of the Bald Eagle resembles that of the Osprey but is larger; it is from four to nine feet in diameter. One nest which I measured was five feet four inches across and seven feet eight inches in depth. This nest had been occupied for many successive years and was about forty feet from the ground in the top of a partly ruined white oak. One nest in Ohio was used consecutively for thirty-five years, and the accumulation of structural material was estimated to weigh two tons. The nests are made of large sticks with a very shallow bowl of smaller ones, cluttered as a rule with rubbish which accumulates from year to year. Eagles remain mated for life and return to the same nest, adding to it from time to time. Commonly the nest is placed near the top of a tall tree, often a dead one, or in a mountain cliff, usually near water. Two eggs are usually laid, although there may be as many as four; they are white or a soiled creamish yellow, and are about three inches in their longest diameter. The female incubates the eggs for about five weeks, and the young remain in the nest about nine or ten weeks.

The Bald Eagle is a harmless species. Its principal food is dead or dying fish. It seems to have little skill in capturing living fish as does the Osprey. The Eagle secures fresh fish by hectoring the Osprey until it drops its catch; then the Eagle swiftly swoops below it and snatches the fish before it reaches the ground. Occasionally eagles feed upon mice, rats, and other small mammals, waterfowl, some game birds, and (very seldom) poultry. It is reported to have attacked pigs, young lambs, and young calves, but such attacks are so few as to be virtually negligible. Eagles do not carry off young children. No eagle can rise with a weight greater than eight or ten pounds—probably not even that. Experiments have demonstrated this conclusively.

In the main Bald Eagles are a sluggish, rather pacific race, though of course an individual may occasionally be severely raptorial. They seldom molest smaller birds with the exception of their attacks upon Ospreys. But even then the attack is not with the intent to do the Osprey harm—the Eagles do not injure their own fishermen. When once the Osprey drops its fish, the Eagle pays no more attention to the hawk, nor do eagles bother hawks that are not carrying fish. Though smaller birds do not often molest the eagles, I have often seen crows and various species of hawks harassing eagles awing, the great birds wheeling higher and higher in the sky until their tormentors dropped off one by one and returned to more comfortable altitudes, leaving their majesties in peace. I once saw a Cooper's Hawk dash up from a defile in the White Mountains after an eagle which it followed to so great a height that even in the field of an 8x binocular it finally became a mere speck and finally passed from sight altogether. The eagle continued to wheel and glide upward until it, too, was only barely perceptible. The Golden

Eagle, not the Bald Eagle, was from time immemorial the honored war eagle of American Indians, who paid scant respect to the white-headed species, probably on account of its mode of securing its living.

While the Bald Eagle may not be quite so "noble" in its hunting and feeding as its congener the Golden Eagle, yet its striking pattern of black and white make it a much more attractive species. This majestic bird, our official national emblem, should be jealously guarded from injury by all patriotic citizens. Yet only recently has it been protected by national law. The Committee on Bird Protection of the American Orinthologist's Union says in its 1940 report that: "The American or Bald Eagle, the emblem of the United States, is now protected by Federal law. This protective legislation recently passed Congress and was signed by the President. Its provisions, however, do not apply to Alaska. In 1917 the Legislature of Alaska started a campaign against the American Eagle by paying a bounty of fifty cents a bird. During the first six years, up to 1923, bounties were paid for about 18,000 birds. It is safe to say that a larger number were actually killed, as some must have fallen in inaccessible places, or died after having been wounded, and doubtless many were killed by persons who did not collect the bounty. From 1917 to the present time the number of eagles killed for bounty in Alaska is believed to be at least 100,000! They are now uncommon over vast areas of their range in this Territory."

Formerly Bald Eagles ranged and bred all over the northeastern states, but now their breeding activities are restricted—with some exceptions—to the mountainous and wilder regions of the northern parts of the territory, and to extensive wooded marsh lands like those of southern New Jersey. They are not known to breed in Massachusetts, Rhode Island, or Connecticut, though I have seen them among the higher mountains of the northwestern corner of Connecticut, where perchance they may still be breeding. Since the birds are great rovers, however, they may be seen almost anywhere in the Northeast. They are common as migrants in the spring or fall, and many individuals may be seen in their great migratory flights from points of vantage in the White and Green Mountains, the mountains of central and western New England, the Catskills, or along the crests of the Alleghenies southward—particularly at Hawk Mountain in Drehersville, Pennsylvania. They winter commonly along the seacoast and the Hudson River, becoming progressively more common southwards.

17

Northern Bald Eagle

wwwwwwwwwwwwwwwwwwwwwwwwwwwwwwwwwwwwwwwwwwwwwwwwwwwwwwww

HALIAEËTUS LEUCOCEPHALUS ALASCANUS

ALSO CALLED

*Bald Eagle, White-Tailed Eagle, White-headed Eagle,
Black Eagle, Gray Eagle* (referring to the young), *Sea
Eagle, Alaskan Eagle, Washington Eagle, Old Abe,
Bird of Freedom, American Eagle, Bald-Headed Eagle*

ADULTS Head, neck, and tail pure white; rest of plumage varying from sooty brown to nearly black. Tarsi partly feathered; bill and feet yellow.

YOUNG Sooty brown, varied with white, gray, and black. Bill black.

BODY LENGTH	WINGSPREAD
Male, 34½ to 43 inches	Male, 82 to 98½ inches
Female, 40 inches or more	Female, 90 inches or more

In habits, form, and coloration, this boreal giant among birds is the counterpart of its smaller conspecies, the Southern Bald Eagle (*see* page 76). The Northern Bald Eagle is probably the largest bird of prey in the northeastern states, sometimes weighing fifteen pounds. It breeds in the northern half of Canada from northwestern Alaska to Labrador and descends in winter into the coastal regions of Maine, less often into those of Massachusetts, and least often as far as the Connecticut coast.

82

Forbush says of the Northern Bald Eagle, "Possibly the majority of wintering New England Bald Eagles may be referred to this subspecies, but many certainly cannot be, as I have measured some very small ones. Probably the large eagles that winter along the Maine coast are referable to this race."

THE FALCONS

(*Family Falconidae*)

GYRFALCONS, among the most adept fliers known, take their rapid course through the air in periods of sailing on set wings alternated with rapid wing strokes. Their food consists of grouse, ptarmigan, murres, puffins, ducks, geese, guillemots, dovekies, gulls, terns, and various species of shore birds, together with lemmings, hares and rabbits, meadow mice, shrews, and other small mammals. From some isolated observations it appears that the birds are not at all averse to a domestic fowl now and then when one is to be had, but the very great rarity of gyrfalcons within our borders prevents them from being factors of any economic importance.

These magnificent falcons appeal strongly to all students and lovers of nature. Their very great beauty should protect them at all times from hunters.

Gyrfalcons deposit their eggs on high cliffs, on ledges, or sometimes in a bulky nest of sticks after the manner of other hawks, though in this latter case the deserted nest of some other bird may be so utilized. The eggs, from two to four in number, are white,

85

creamy, pinkish, light brown to cinnamon brown, thickly marked with various shades of brown or dark gray.

Of the five species of gyrfalcons known three are North American, and two found in the Northeast. They are all subspecies of *Falco rusticolus*. All gradations of plumage occur between the white and the black species, and their relationships are still problematical. A. C. Bent says of the group: "The gyrfalcons have always been a very puzzling group; their nomenclature has been confusing; their relationships have never been well understood; and confusion as to the distribution of the different forms has been even worse. Various views on all these points have been expressed by different writers, but none of them are conclusive or wholly satisfactory. Until we have available a considerable series of breeding birds, both adults and their young, collected in various parts of the breeding ranges, we shall never fully understand the relationships of the various forms and their ranges. Most of the specimens in collections are late fall or winter birds, which may have wandered far from their native ranges. Even summer specimens are not necessarily breeding birds, as immature birds and nonbreeding adults are often widely scattered in summer. We need also a series of young birds in juvenile plumage, taken before, or soon after, the flight stage is reached, to help us recognize with certainty the immature plumage of the different races."

18

Black Gyrfalcon

~~~~~~

FALCO RUSTICOLUS OBSOLETUS

ALSO CALLED

*Brown Gyrfalcon, Black Falcon, Gray
Gyrfalcon, Labrador Gyrfalcon,
Labrador Falcon*

ADULTS Upper parts dark slate grayish-brown, sometimes almost black; very variable. Edges of the feathers zoned with lighter shades. Under parts similar, or with edges of feathers broader and lighter, sometimes white.

YOUNG Similar to the adults, but more prominently streaked with lighter shades; flanks and the feathers of the legs spotted with white.

BODY LENGTH	*WINGSPREAD*
Male, 21 inches	Male, 47 inches
Female, 23 inches	Female, 52 inches

The Black Gyrfalcon is a very rare winter visitant in the New England States, less than two score individuals having been recorded during the past sixty years. The bird breeds in northern North America from Alaska to Labrador.

In flight it somewhat resembles the Duck Hawk, but is darker (sometimes almost black) and larger by some five inches from bill to tail.

19

White Gyrfalcon

FALCO RUSTICOLUS CANDICANS

ALSO CALLED

Gray Gyrfalcon, Greenland Falcon, Winter Falcon,
White Hawk, Winterer, White Winter Hawk

ADULTS Upper parts white, the plumage of the head and neck finely streaked, cross-barred or spotted more heavily on the back with slate- and brownish-gray. Under parts usually unmarked white, sometimes finely spotted on the sides with dusky.

YOUNG Similar to the adults, but with the dark markings on the back somewhat lighter and arranged in elongated spots or streaks and not as crossbars.

BODY LENGTH	*WINGSPREAD*
Male, 21 to 22½ inches	Male, 48 to 49 inches
Female, 23 to 24 inches	Female, 49 to 51 inches

The White Gyrfalcon is our only white hawk and, with the single exception of the Snowy Owl, our only white bird of prey.

This beautiful falcon is unfortunately only an accidental visitor in the extreme northern part of our territory, only a single specimen having been taken, at South Winn, Maine, in October, 1893. It breeds chiefly in the arctic regions of North America, Greenland, and Asia, and in winter moves southward in the eastern portion of our continent as far as southern Quebec, Nova Scotia, and possibly farther south. There seems to be no reason to doubt that unusually severe winters in its northern range might force the bird to descend in some numbers into the northeastern states. Several individuals have been recorded (but not taken) flying over the Kittatiny Ridge in Pennsylvania.

20
Peregrine Falcon

〰〰〰〰〰〰〰〰〰〰〰〰〰〰〰〰〰〰〰〰〰〰〰〰〰〰〰〰

FALCO PEREGRINUS ANATUM

ALSO CALLED

*Rock Falcon, Great-Footed Falcon, Rock
Hawk, Stone Hawk, Ledge Hawk, Wan-
dering Falcon, Big Blue Hawk, Blue Bullet
Hawk, Black-Cheeked Hawk, Duck Hawk,
American Peregrine, Mountain Falcon*

ADULTS Upper parts dark bluish slaty-gray, the primaries
barred with light reddish-brown. Dark "mustache markings" at
the base of the bill. Tail faintly barred with black and tipped with
white. Under parts creamy or yellowish-buff, barred and spotted
with black except on the breast.

YOUNG Upper parts dark grayish-brown, the feathers somewhat
margined with light or dark reddish-brown. The "mustache markings" are brown. Upper surface of tail barred with gray; under surface barred with light reddish-buff. Under parts creamy buff,
streaked, spotted, or barred with black.

BODY LENGTH	*WINGSPREAD*
Male, 15 to 18 inches	Male, 38½ to 43 inches
Female, 18 to 20 inches	Female, 43 to 46 inches

The Duck Hawk or American Peregrine is our New World counterpart of the Old World "noble peregrine" or "falcon gentil,"

91

so much prized as a hawking bird by the chivalry of the Middle Ages. No one has painted a better word portrait of the bird than G. H. Thayer, who says, "It is perhaps the most highly specialized and superlatively well-developed flying organism on our planet to-day, combining in a marvellous degree the highest powers of speed and aerial adroitness with massive war-like strength. A powerful, wild, majestic, independent bird, living on the choicest of clean carnal food plucked fresh from the air or the surface of the waters; rearing its young in the nooks of dangerous mountain cliffs; claiming all the atmosphere as its domain, and fearing neither beast that walks nor bird that flies—it is the very embodiment of noble rapacity and lonely freedom. It has its legitimate and important place in the great scheme of things, and by its extermination—if that should ever come—the whole world would be impoverished and dulled."

In its powers of flight the Peregrine Falcon is unequalled by any other bird. It can easily overtake that rapid flier, the Chimney Swift, and only by means of quick twists and dodging can the quarry elude its rush. Rising to a considerable height above its intended victim, the Peregrine Falcon plunges downward with hissing velocity and strikes a lightning-like, mortal blow that sends its victim hurtling dead to earth. Or it may swoop alongside or ahead of some bird in the full headlong flight of terror and, suddenly reaching out, snatch it out of mid-air with one foot. One grip of those powerful, sharp, curved talons means immediate death. Whether it strikes a blow or grasps, the Peregrine Falcon's killing is instantaneous. Sometimes it swoops upon its quarry on the surface of the water.

Small birds of all species (except the very smallest warblers, kinglets, titmice, and the like) constitute about one-half its food, and larger birds about one-third. Among the latter may be mentioned such forms as the Blue Jay (of which it is especially fond), Crow, Belted Kingfisher, Flicker, various species of ducks, grebes, and similar forms; snipe, sandpipers, pigeons, pheasants, grouse, and when occasion offers, poultry. Since it is pre-eminently a bird of the wild, however, it does not often invade the precincts of the farm. A considerable number of large flying insects such as grasshoppers, beetles, and dragonflies are taken, and some few mice and other small mammals. Birds, however, taken awing constitute its chief food. As a predator its value in its own wild domain is unquestioned. As a resident near a farm or a game preserve, it is not so desirable.

It would seem unaccountable that some sportsmen can censure so fine a bird as this noble falcon! For the falcon is a hunter too, but with these differences: the falcon hunts only for its necessary food, and this is its only method of securing it. It has no other source of food supply. It does not hunt for "sport," that is, to gratify the desire to kill something. Furthermore the falcon pursues its prey in open flight—armed only with its own wings and talons. It does not hide and skulk in blinds and deceive its victims with decoys and false calls—its hunting is based upon honor, not deception. Moreover the falcon does not wound without killing. None of its victims crawl away lacerated to die a lingering death.

Peregrine Falcons make no nests as a rule but deposit their eggs usually on a shelf or rock high up on a cliff face, among mountains, in such a situation as gives a wide vista over a river valley, lake, or seashore. Nests have infrequently been found lodged in the scraggy tops of broken trees. The birds may become very much attached to their nesting locality and return to the same spot for many successive years. The eggs, from two to six (rarely) in number, vary from creamy white, heavily marked with flecks and blotches of reddish-brown, to an almost uniformly light reddish-brown marked sparsely or not at all.

Peregrine Falcons are not much given to vocalization. Their notes are shrill and harsh. When the locality of the nest is invaded, the birds fly back and forth along the face of the rocks uttering loud, screaming, discordant cries.

The long pointed wings, slender tail, and the black "mustache markings" are the distinguishing physical features of the Peregrine

94

Falcon. Its flight is characteristic. The quick, slashing wing beats are executed below the body as well as above it.

The Peregrine Falcon is a rare summer resident and breeding bird throughout our northeastern states, and confines itself to mountains or high hilly regions wherever there are bare, precipitous cliffs. Thus its occurrence is local. It is found, for example, in such regions as northern and western Maine, various parts of the White Mountains and Green Mountains, Mount Monadnock in southern New Hampshire, in the Berkshires, in the mountains along the Connecticut Valley, and as far south as Meriden Mountain in southern Connecticut. In Rhode Island the bird is a rare migrant, chiefly along the coast. In New York and New Jersey Peregrine Falcons are found principally along the Palisades (they are sometimes seen in New York City capturing pigeons) and in the mountains farther to the north, in the Adirondacks, and in some other localities. One pair, made famous by Dr. A. A. Allen of Cornell University, nested in the precipitous wall of the gorge of Taughannock Creek near Ithaca.

21

Eastern Pigeon Hawk

wwwwwwwwwwwwwwwwwwwwwwwwwwwwwwwwwwwwwwwwwwwwwwwwwwwwwwwwwwwwwwwwwwwww

FALCO COLUMBARIUS COLUMBARIUS

ALSO CALLED

Pigeon Hawk, American Merlin,
Little Corporal, Blue Bullet Hawk

ADULTS Upper parts slaty blue, the irregular buff collar about the neck streaked with the same color. Primaries barred with white. Slaty-blue tail tipped with white and crossed by three or four whitish bars. Under parts varying from a light cream to a creamy buff or often a light reddish-brown and streaked with blackish, except on the throat, which is often white or grayish.

YOUNG Upper parts dark grayish-brown, the irregular collar about the neck streaked with the same color. Primaries barred with light reddish-brown. Dark tail with whitish tip and crossed by three or four incomplete narrow buff bars. Under parts virtually the same as in the adults.

BODY LENGTH	*WINGSPREAD*
Male, 10 to 10½ inches	Male, 20 to 22 inches
Female, 12 to 13½ inches	Female, 24 to 26½ inches

Like its close relative, the Sparrow Hawk, the diminutive bluish Pigeon Hawk may frequently be seen perched on the topmost twig of a small tree, on a post, or on a telephone pole, where it motionlessly surveys the terrain round about. Suddenly it launches itself

into the air like the flash of an arrow and makes off after some passing finch or warbler, or drops like a plummet to the grass, there to strike its talons into a large insect or Meadow Mouse. Its powers of flight are remarkable. The fact that it is able to pursue and to capture dragonflies on the wing attests to the rapidity and dexterity of its movements.

Breeding chiefly north of the northeastern states, it nevertheless occurs as a rare nesting bird in the mountains of northern Maine as well as in the northernmost mountains of Vermont, New Hampshire, and New York. It spends the winter in small numbers, rarely on the southern coast of Maine, in the coastal portions of the other New England states, on Long Island, and in New Jersey. Over the Northeast in general, however, it is to be regarded chiefly as a fairly common spring and fall migrant.

Pigeon Hawks' nests are usually to be found from eight to forty or fifty feet from the ground, more often in pines, spruces, hemlocks, or other coniferous trees than in deciduous ones. Occasionally a nest will be discovered tucked away on a shelf in the face of a rocky cliff or hidden in a hollow tree. In such situations very little nesting material is used. The tree nests are composed of sticks and twigs, and lined with smaller twigs, strips of bark, weed stems, coarse grasses, often with the addition of leaves, moss, and some hair. The eggs, from four to seven in number, vary from white through all shades to a deep purplish-brown and are blotched and spotted with darker brown.

Like most hawks, the Pigeon Hawk gives voice to sharp and squealing notes. Its commonest utterance sounds like the highly pitched syllables, *ke-reeee, ke-reeeee*. When disturbed or greatly elated, its notes are a loud *kek, kek, kek, kek,* though on the whole it is a relatively silent bird.

Small birds form the largest proportion of the food of this rapacious little falcon and constitute nearly three-quarters of its diet. Insects rank next in importance, forming about one-quarter of its food. These are chiefly such large forms as beetles, grasshoppers, and crickets. Mice (chiefly Meadow Mice) together with poultry and game birds do not constitute more than about one-twelfth of its diet. Sometimes the bird may become a local pest through its depredations among pigeons and less frequently among young domestic poultry. In its considerable destruction of insects and similar, though lesser, effectiveness with respect to Meadow Mice it is decidedly the ally of the farmer. Its capture of the smaller song and insectivorous birds is restricted in large measure to the weaker individuals, and hence it is to be looked upon as beneficial to these groups.

The Pigeon Hawk and the Sparrow Hawk are somewhat similar. However the Pigeon Hawk may be distinguished from the Sparrow Hawk by its slightly greater size, its uniformly darker bluish-gray back, and its lack of vertical black markings on the side of the head. The tail of the adult Pigeon Hawk is a dark bluish-gray with several prominent white or whitish crossbars, whereas the tail of the Sparrow Hawk is predominantly light brown. In all plumages the Pigeon Hawk is appreciably the darker bird of the two. From the Sharp-Shinned Hawk the Pigeon Hawk may be distinguished by its pointed rather than rounded wings.

22

Eastern Sparrow Hawk

〜〜〜〜〜〜〜〜〜〜〜〜〜〜〜〜〜〜〜〜〜〜〜〜〜〜〜〜〜〜

FALCO SPARVERIUS SPARVERIUS

ALSO CALLED

Killy Hawk, Grasshopper Falcon, Grasshopper Hawk, Rusty-Crowned Falcon, American Kestrel, Mouse Hawk

ADULT MALE Back rich reddish-brown somewhat barred with black. Tail similar, tipped first with a narrow white, then with a broader black band. Head slate blue; crown reddish-brown. Sides of head, white, marked with vertical black bars. Wings slaty blue, their primaries barred with white. Under parts varying from creamy buff to light reddish-brown. Sides of breast and abdomen prominently spotted with black.

ADULT FEMALE Back, tail, and wing coverts reddish-brown barred with black. Head similar to that of the male. Under parts more or less heavily streaked with reddish-brown.

YOUNG Similar to the adults.

BODY LENGTH	WINGSPREAD
Male, 8¾ to 10⅝ inches	Male, 20 to 22 inches
Female, 9 to 12 inches	Female, 23 to 24 inches

An opportunist, it is said, is a person who when he finds himself in hot water, proceeds to take a bath. If adaptability to alimentary

circumstances be the criterion for determining an optimist, then surely the Sparrow Hawk well merits the appellation. More, perhaps, than any other of our hawk species does this diminutive little bird of prey change its diet with the exigencies of seasons or other natural conditions. Feeding largely on insects during the months when these are abundant, it turns its attention in the fall to mice and other small rodents. In winter, when snow and ice invest its territory, small birds engage its notice. In the vicinity of towns these small birds are very apt to be English Sparrows or Starlings, and in the woods and fields such forms as Juncos, Tree Sparrows and other small finches, as well as woodpeckers, nuthatches, chickadees, and the like.

It is unfortunate that this very desirable little falcon labors under a complete misnomer. No more unfair appellation than *Sparrow Hawk* could be devised to stigmatize a creature less than one-eighth of whose food consists of small birds. Meadow Mice and other mouse species form a quarter of its diet, while insects, chiefly large forms such as beetles, crickets, and grasshoppers make up one-half. In view of a menu of this character, the names Grasshopper Hawk or Grasshopper Falcon are much more appropriate. The bird is so very common, so widespread in its distribution, and so very unsuspicious and easy of observation that there would seem to be little excuse for ignorance of its habits and food. It is not difficult to study the bird's feeding habits with field glasses and to identify many of the forms which it may be seen to capture. It has been alleged that these hawks attack young chickens, but creditable records are so infrequent as to be negligible. When Sparrow Hawks are observed about farm buildings, it is usually because they are then preying upon House Mice. Many of these rodents are caught in the neighborhood of corn stacks, granaries, and other storehouses.

The Sparrow Hawk or Rusty-Crowned Falcon—to call the bird by a more fitting name—is not only the smallest of our hawks (the male is about the size of a Robin). It is also the most brightly colored. These colors, however, are not often seen to their best advantage, since when the bird is observed it is usually either perched above the level of the eye or of the horizon line or else it is in flight, in both of which circumstances not only is the bright-colored back concealed from the view of the observer below, but the whole bird appears more as a dark silhouette by reason of its background of bright sky.

Sparrow Hawks are birds of "broken" country, that is, territory of interspersed meadows, woodlands, fields, farm lands, groves—in fact, everywhere except in deep forests, high mountains, or shores. It flies with an easy grace not so much suggestive of dash and vigor as of lightness and dexterity. It customarily perches on some coign of vantage, as upon the topmost twig of a tree, the top of a telephone pole, or on a wire, and just after alighting usually pumps its tail several times after the manner of the Phoebe. Occasionally, just after settling upon its perch, it folds and refolds its long graceful wings with a delicate and meticulous precision. Its most pleasing and characteristic habit, however, is its habit of hovering in one spot in the air with rapidly beating wings, its body remaining like a fixed dot in the sky as though suspended by an invisible wire. During such intervals its keen vision is scanning the terrain below for a possible tidbit hidden in the grass.

The term Killy Hawk, frequently applied to the bird, refers to its commonest notes, a series of high, shrill, piping, not unpleasing calls sounding like the syllables *killy, killy, killy, killy*. Or it may scream *kee-kee, kee-kee,* notes reminiscent of the Kildeer Plover's call. When the nest is attacked the birds scream loudly and harshly or utter the abrupt *cac, cac, cac* notes so common to hawks in general.

The Killy Hawk has taken kindly to man's usurpation of its domain and nests familiarly in the neighborhood of his dwellings, sometimes building its nest in the nook of some outbuilding or often in a bird box if it be suitably built and placed. Under natural conditions the nest is hidden in the cavity of a tree, frequently in a deserted Flicker's hole, or tucked away in a rocky cliff or hole in a bank. No nesting material is brought into the cavity, the eggs being deposited on whatever debris happens to be present.

From four to seven eggs comprise the set. They are sub-oval to almost spherical in form and vary considerably in color from white through cream to a yellowish or light reddish-brown, blotched, spotted, and mottled with various shades of browns, grays, and lavenders.

In flight the Sparrow Hawk may be recognized by its long, pointed, crescentic wings and long tail and by its habit of hovering. When perched, the diminutive size of both sexes, the brilliant colors of the male, and the plain pale reddish-brown back of the female are helpful for identification.

The Sparrow Hawk breeds more generally throughout the Northeast than any other hawk. One encounters it progressively less in the higher mountains of the north. It winters fairly commonly throughout the northeastern states except in the extreme northern and central portions.

THE OWLS

(Families Tytonidae and Strigidae)

TO MOST human beings owls are feathered mysteries; to mice they are feathered mousetraps; and when in pursuit of any of their prey they are feathered bolts of lightning. It is not surprising that owls, of all our native birds, are the least understood. They are seldom seen and not very frequently heard. They are not very numerous; with some exceptions they inhabit wild or sparsely settled country; they are abroad chiefly at night or in the early hours of morning or evening twilight; and finally they are by nature silent, furtive, and not so much given to vocal performances as most of our smaller diurnal birds. Despite their secretive habits, owls are fairly common birds, but like elves and fairies "they work and play while weary households sleep, and seldom allow themselves to be seen by mortal eyes."

To many watchers of the fields and woods owls are of interest if only because of their secretive habits and the difficulties involved in studying them and because of their long associations in literature and legend with all that is eerie, portentous, and occult. From the

105

earliest times owls have been by common report invested with other-world powers of prophecy, uncanny prescience and wisdom, and have frequently been associated with the gods. Pallas Athene of the Greeks (Minerva of the Romans) is represented in art as being attended by the Little Mediterranean Owl, the European counterpart of our Screech Owl, as her special bird.

> "O you virtuous owle,
> The wise Minerva's only fowle."

Owls have also been regarded as associates of sorcerers, necromancers, and astrologers. They have been supposed to be the familiar attendants upon ghosts, hobgoblins, and all the spectral inhabitants of the world of phantoms, and in their character as banshees and dire apparitions were thought to wail and shriek in notes quite other than their own natural tones. The Elder Pliny stigmatizes the whole tribe as presagers of death and woe. Isaiah uses them as symbols of all that is reminiscent of ruin, misery, desolation, and decay: "And thorns shall come up in her palaces; nettles and brambles in the fortresses thereof; and it shall be an habitation of dragons, and a court for owls."

The voices of owls, those eerie, discordant, nocturnal hootings, gobblings, and screamings uttered by so many species have been regarded as predictions or actual causes of the inescapable approach of disaster, illness, and death. The colored folk of our southern states have many tales of owls' causal alliance with personal misfortune. Many an old mammy and gray-haired patriarch still aver their ability to foretell from the character of the voices of owls the exact nature of the evils about to ensue. An old negro in Mississippi observed to the writer, "Ef yo' heahs a squinch owl tootin' just befo' de moon comes up, look out fo' yo'self. But ef yo' heahs him just *after* de moon is up, den look out fo' de oldes' one of yo' kinfolk." In the medieval pharmacopoeia various parts of the anatomy of owls were prescribed as medicines of great potency, and even as late as

1819 in our own country, a book entitled *The Long Hidden Friend,* published in German in Reading, Pennsylvania, soberly admonished its readers thus: "If you lay the heart and right foot of a Barn Owl on one who is asleep, he will answer whatever you ask him, and tell what he has done."

The multitude of the references to owls in English literature makes a fascinating study. Shakespeare is full of such references, especially to owls as trouble makers and prophets of gloom, and so are the older English writers generally. The most familiar appearance of these birds in Shakespeare is perhaps in *Macbeth,* where the "howlet's wing" was listed as an important ingredient of that "charm of powerful trouble" stewed up in the caldron of the three witches on the desert heath. After the murder of King Duncan, Macbeth comes in exclaiming, "I have done the deed; didst thou hear a noise?" To which Lady Macbeth replies, "I heard the owl scream, and the crickets cry." "Out on ye, owls," cries Richard Third, "nothing but songs of death!"

The poets from Chatterton down have used owls and their cries freely to enhance the scenes of horror they wish to depict.

In spite of all this, there is no group of wild creatures that deserves better at our hands than the owls, for they take high rank among our most economically valuable birds. Their food consists almost entirely of mice and other small rodents, creatures which are woefully destructive of crop plants, of orchard and other trees, and of the stored products of agriculture generally. Hence we owe to our native owls full protection and a fair opportunity "for life, liberty, and the pursuit of" mice. We owe to them complete security from such agencies of destruction as the barbaric pole trap and the shotgun. Only the Great Horned Owl would seem not to merit our favor and protection. But read his record on pages 146–147. Sportsmen object seriously to the Great Horned Owl, and their objections are based on the ground that it kills what they themselves wish to kill. The owl does this not for sport, however, but for necessary food. There appears here to be a difference, a difference which leaves in the thoughtful mind a balance of sympathy in favor of the wild creature.

Dr. A. K. Fisher and his staff, formerly of our Federal Bureau of Biological Survey, now the Fish and Wildlife Service of the Department of Agriculture, had earlier studied and recorded their observations of the content of the stomachs, crops, and pellets of more than 2,700 individual hawks and owls including all our native species, taken from every portion of our country, and representing every season of the year. Pellets are compact balls made up of the indigestible portions of the food: bones, fur, feathers, etc., cast out of the mouth before absorption begins. Of this exhaustive study Dr. Fisher said, "The result proves that this class of birds, commonly looked upon as enemies to the farmer, and indiscriminately destroyed whenever occasion offers, really rank among his best friends, and with few exceptions should be preserved."

The examination of the contents of crops, stomachs, and pellets, correlated with studies in the field principally in the New England States and New Jersey, made by the writer and combined with similar studies by ornithologists in other portions of our country, substantiate this conclusion. Owls—and in fact our birds of prey in general—are the friends, not the foes, of mankind. During most of their waking hours these tireless birds are ceaselessly engaged in a hunt for food, and this food consists of those very pests which man himself is glad to see kept in proper check.

Owls fly about and swoop upon their prey almost without a sound, for their feathers are unusually soft and fluffy, and produce no whistling or swishing noises as the birds sweep through the air. The Indian name of "hush-wing" refers to this unique inaudible character of their flight.

In general owls hunt by night (the nocturnal hunters), or in the dim and shadowy hours of morning and evening twilight (the crepuscular hunters); but some species like the Snowy Owl and Hawk Owl habitually hunt by day (the diurnal hunters). All owls, however, when under the severe press of hunger or when the young are in the nest and especially clamorous for food, may engage in hunting by day, particularly on days which are dark and cloudy.

It is not true that owls are unable to see in the daylight. They can see very well indeed, but not so well as in the dusk. In strong light the iris diaphragm of the eye nearly closes to protect the sensitive retina from too great a stimulation, but as evening approaches and as the light diminishes, the diaphragm opens progressively wider, and as it does so, the eye appears as a large, luminous dark orb. The wider open the iris is, the more light is permitted to pass through the lens to the retina or sensitive tissue at the back of the eyeball where the image is focussed. It is only to the owls, not to the hawks, that a dimmer illumination is more agreeable. In fact some of the hawk tribe have been reputed to be able unflinchingly to gaze directly upon the flaming orb of an unclouded sun itself.

> Creatures there be of sight so keen and high
> That even to the sun they bend their gaze;
> But others, dazzled by too fierce a blaze,
> Issue not forth till evening veils the sky.
> PETRARCH

It is probable that owls are incapable of distinguishing the short-wave colors blue, purple, and indigo, and are conscious only of the long-wave ones of red, orange, yellow, and green. It is supposed that they are particularly sensitive to the longest visible vibrations at the red end of the spectrum and that the retina may be affected even by infrared radiation, a radiation not perceptible to our eyes. This supposition is correlated with the birds' preference for twilight and even murkier hours.

The eyes of many crepuscular and nocturnal creatures emit a peculiar light at night which primitive peoples believed was of the animal's own volition and production. The American Indians had noted this nocturnal peculiarity of the eyes of owls in particular and averred that the eyes themselves were the source of the emitted light. This belief is alluded to in Longfellow's *Song of Hiawatha*, where the poet makes old Nokomis sing in her lullaby to the infant Hiawatha:

"Ewa-yea! My little owlet,
Who is this that lights the wigwam?
With his great eyes lights the wigwam?
Ewa-yea! My little owlet."

Walker, in his "Eyes that Shine at Night" (*Annual Report,* Smithsonian Institution, Washington, 1938), points out that the eyes of birds of prey, like those of many mammals, shine at night but only by reflected light, producing different colors. It is probable that the striated or laminated nature of the structures of the eye refracts the gathered light much after the manner of a diffraction grating or thin-film apparatus. The eyes of the Red-Shouldered Hawk are reported to emit a faint silvery reflection; those of the Great Horned Owl a brilliant golden, orange-red, or greenish-gold hue; those of the Barred Owl a deep vibrant gold or orange; and those of the Screech Owl a ruby red. All these eye-shines are brilliant and lustrous; they seem to flash in a divergent manner and to resemble "small incandescent lights seen at a distance."

The eye of an owl is probably the most efficient organ of vision in the world. It not only functions as a most perfect light-gathering mechanism, but also can be focused so as to become either a telescope or a microscope at a moment's notice, literally "in the twinkling of an eye." The structures which make all this possible in the eyes of both hawks and owls, are discussed on pages xxi–xxii.

Though some owls appear lethargic or even stupid during the hours of daylight, yet when evening approaches and their prey begins to stir abroad, they become progressively the most alert and vigilant of all wild creatures, and when perched, keep their heads constantly swinging from side to side as they scan every inch of the terrain beneath them. The ability of an owl to turn its head is noteworthy and forms a distinct adaptation to its predatory habit. The cervical or neck vertebrae of an owl give so much flexibility of motion to the head that the bird is capable of rotating this part of its body through nearly 180 degrees of an arc, that is to say, of being able to turn its head so as to stare straight backwards over its shoulder blades.

Owls are so protectively colored and patterned that while hiding by day amid heavy foliage, among thickly growing branches, or in the hollow of a tree, they often completely escape detection. Their prevailing colors are gray, brown, dull yellow, and buff, marked with various patterns of black. The great northern Snowy Owl, however, is white, a hue according well with its surroundings of ice and snow. Owls sit motionless for long periods of time and thus become, for all purposes of concealment, almost a part of the tree itself. This habit, together with their obliterative coloration, makes the birds appear like broken upright stubs, a resemblance which is strengthened in some species by the presence of erect tufts of feathers on the head popularly known as "horns" or "ears."

These feathers, however, have nothing to do with the bird's organs of hearing, which are in general much like our own except for the absence of outwardly projecting shells or pinnae. The pinna or shell of an owl's ear consists of a low ridge of skin extending from over the eye around the back border of the facial disc, a structure which terminates in the neighborhood of the base of the bill. The canal of the ear opens into the skull just behind and below the eyesocket and together with the pinna is covered and completely concealed, in the adult bird, partly by the feathers of the facial disc and partly by tufts of feathers just behind these. All this does not appear to constitute a very effective mechanism for the capture of sound waves; nevertheless the fact remains that the sense of hearing in owls is singularly acute and serves the birds well in their detection of prey during those dusky hours when vision must seek aid from another sense. The slightest rustle in the grass does not escape the keen ears of a listening owl. None of the small wood folk can hope to tread so softly as to escape discovery. "As still as a mouse" is an adage which makes no sense at all to Old Hush Wing, the Owl.

111

In some respects owls resemble hawks, particularly in the possession of strongly hooked beaks, powerful wings, and long curved talons, but their anatomical relationships ally them much more closely with the *Caprimulgiformes,* represented in our country by such species as the Nighthawk, Whip-poor-will, and Chuck-Will's Widow.

Owls' heads appear large both because of the fluffy character of the feathers and because of the presence of the facial discs or radiating circles of feathers about the large eyes. The uncanny "stary" expression of an owl's face is accentuated by the character of the eyes, which are set immovably in the front of the skull and cannot be rolled from side to side. The owl therefore has but a single field of vision, a field lying straight ahead and regarded by both eyes at once, as in the human species, the sort of vision known as binocular vision. Other birds, in which the eyes are set one on each side of the head, possess two fields of vision, one for each eye, a type of vision known as monocular vision.

In their breeding activities owls are of especial interest because in latitudes of the northeastern states some are the first birds to nest in the spring, the Great Horned Owl occasionally depositing its eggs as early as the first week of February. Some owls breed in cavities in trees, in niches in cliffs, or, in the case of the Barn Owl, in old buildings, without the construction of a nest; other species make use of the deserted nests of crows, hawks, or squirrels. The Snowy Owl and the Short-Eared Owl deposit their eggs in crude nests placed on the ground.

As articles of food owls have never been highly esteemed. They were proscribed to the early Hebrews in the laws of Moses and Aaron: "And these are they which ye shall have in abomination among the fowls; they shall not be eaten: the eagle . . . and the ospray . . . the vulture and the kite . . . the raven . . . the owl, the nighthawk and the cuckow . . . the hawk . . . the little owl, the cormorant, and the great owl."

Because of their great size, however, the larger owls have sometimes been shot for food, though probably without much subsequent gastronomic satisfaction if one may judge from the New England dictum "tougher than a biled owl," which in rural districts is a phrase descriptive of the acme of all that is resistant to mastication. The writer has never tasted the flesh of an owl, though it would seem that few persons, after a first experience, would again have the hardihood to "bile" an owl with the intention of eating it afterwards!

Owls are distributed all over the world, over five hundred species and subspecies being known at the present time. In North America fifty-six species and subspecies are found, and in the northeastern states are thirteen species and subspecies grouped into two families, the Family *Tytonidae* (Barn Owls) , and the Family *Strigidae* (typical owls) .

23

Barn Owl

∿∿

TYTO ALBA PRATINCOLA

ADULTS Upper parts buffy-yellow finely marked with black, white, and gray. Tail yellowish flecked with black and in some instances bearing three or four indistinct black bars. Under parts white or straw-yellow sprinkled with fine black dots. Facial discs whitish or yellowish deepening to light brownish around the eyes, and outlined with deep yellowish-brown. Iris of eyes and bill, black. Female usually larger than the male, rarely smaller.

BODY LENGTH	*WINGSPREAD*
15 to 21 inches	43¼ to 47 inches

The Barn Owl is seldom seen in daylight except as it may be chanced upon while roosting in the dark corner of some old building or among the thick foliage of an evergreen. When disturbed in such a situation it makes off clumsily in an uncertain and irregular flight, as though bewildered both by the intrusion and by the light into which it has been driven. At night, however, the bird is anything but uncertain and bewildered; possessed of unusually acute night sight and served by large and especially sensitive ears, it glides swiftly, unerringly, and noiselessly upon its prey, aided in this sort of spectral locomotion by its extremely light and downy plumage which enables it to fly without the noise of whistling pinions which stiffer feathers would occasion. This eerie sort of flight and the habit of nesting in deserted buildings, old towers and steeples, and ghostly ruins have resulted in the bird's being taken more than once for the "haunt" or spirit of such localities, more especially since one

114

of its common flight notes is a weird, somewhat subdued, hissing scream. Other utterances include a series of clicks and clucks and guttural gobblings, together with weak and querulous whining notes, all of which are more suggestive of the world of phantoms than of our own.

The Barn Owl nests in almost any situation which affords adequate shelter, most commonly in old barns and outbuildings, in church towers and old steeples, and ruins of all sorts. Holes in banks, or under cliffs, or occasionally hollow trees, or more rarely a deserted hawk's nest may also be used. The eggs are deposited either upon a bare surface or amid a collection of rubbish, sticks, or chips, or upon a pile of bones, fur, and feathers ejected from the mouths of the young birds of previous broods. The eggs number from five to eight, and in the Northeast are laid about the last week of April.

The Barn Owl is one of our most beneficial birds of prey. Since it nests most frequently in the vicinity of man's dwellings, on the edges of towns, or about farm buildings, the greater bulk of its food consists of domestic mice and rats. Barn Owls seldom feed on small birds, and when they do it is seldom in quantity. Forty-two pellets collected by the writer under a water tower on the edge of New Brunswick, New Jersey, where a pair of these owls were nesting, were composed entirely of the fur and bones of domestic mice and rats. No bird remains were found in these pellets in spite of the fact that English Sparrows and Starlings were especially numerous in the immediate vicinity of the nest. Among the mammals in the bird's diet are the Domestic Rat, the House Mouse, the Pine Mouse, the Jumping Mouse, the Meadow Mouse, the Deer Mouse, the Short-Tailed Shrew, the Star-Nosed Mole, and the Common Mole. Bats are occasionally eaten. The insects devoured include cicadas, katydids, grasshoppers (locusts), and crickets. Among the birds which are infrequently eaten may be mentioned the Cowbird, the Vesper Sparrow, the English Sparrow, and the Starling.

In New England and northern New York the Barn Owl is decidedly a rarity. It is known only as an accidental visitor in Vermont and New Hampshire, but increases somewhat in numbers southwards into Connecticut. It is found in the Genesee Valley in New York as well as on Long Island and Staten Island. In northern New Jersey it occurs as a rare permanent resident, but is found more commonly in the southern part of the state.

When perched, the Barn Owl may be recognized by its generally light buffy-yellowish-white color, prominent light-colored facial discs, and long legs. When in flight its whitish under parts are diagnostic, the only other owl showing light-colored under parts being the Snowy Owl.

24

Long-Eared Owl

〜〜〜〜〜〜〜〜〜〜〜〜〜〜〜〜〜〜〜〜〜〜〜〜〜〜〜〜〜〜〜〜〜〜

ASIO OTUS WILSONIANUS

ADULTS Upper parts grayish-brown marked with whitish- and yellowish-brown. Breast whitish with heavy streaks of dark brownish-gray; abdomen and sides heavily streaked and crossbarred with the same color. The conspicuous ear-tufts, an inch or so long, are blackish, bordered by yellowish-brown and white. The facial discs are reddish-brown bordered with black. Iris of eye, yellow; bill black. Female slightly larger than the male.

BODY LENGTH	*WINGSPREAD*
13 to 16 inches	36 to 42 inches

This owl is our slenderest and most graceful species. When in flight its long wings and tail make it appear a much larger bird than it actually is, particularly when one sees it, as one does most frequently, in the twilight hours. It is almost exclusively a nocturnal bird, seldom flying abroad except at night or in the deep dusk of morning or evening twilight. During the day it remains concealed amid dark foliage, usually in a grove of coniferous trees, and if disturbed does not ordinarily take flight at once but draws the feathers tightly about the body and stands stiffly erect—habits which, together with its coloration, give it the appearance of a broken, upright stub. Long-Eared Owls nest in the penetralia of deep woodlands, preferably coniferous ones, utilizing the abandoned nests of crows, hawks, or herons, but occasionally building nests of their own. These nests are masses of sticks somewhat resembling the nests of crows and are placed amid thick branches about 25 or 30 feet

from the ground. Sometimes, though not often, the nesting is carried on within a hollow tree, in a hole of a cliff, or even on the ground. From three to seven eggs are laid from about the last week of March to the middle of April.

The notes of the Long-Eared Owl are many, the commonest being a long snarling cat-like *eeeeaaaooow,* or a thin, nasal, querulous cry *eeeeuuuh,* and during the mating season a soft though deep *hoo-ood, hoo-ood.*

The bird is said to make a very amusing and gentle pet, and is easy to tame. It assuredly is one of the easiest of owls to approach in the field, not at all shy of man's presence if one moves quietly and not too rapidly, and is not very easily flushed.

The food of the Long-Eared Owl consists largely of Meadow or Field Mice together with a smaller number of House Mice, Pine Mice, Deer Mice, and shrews. Large beetles form the bulk of the insects food. Small birds constitute a minor part of all that this owl eats; among the species which have been recognized in the stomach contents are the Goldfinch, the Tree Sparrow, the Junco, the Myrtle Warbler, the Golden-Crowned Kinglet, and the Bluebird. Because of the enormous quantities of mice, especially of Field Mice, which the bird devours, it is to be ranked as one of our most beneficial species.

As a breeding bird the Long-Eared Owl is fairly common in the northern half of the northeastern states except in the mountain forests of the Adirondacks of New York and on the higher mountains of New England. It is uncommon in southern Massachusetts, southern New York, Connecticut, Rhode Island, and New Jersey. In the southern half of the area its numbers are considerably augmented by migrating individuals in the spring and fall and by those which come for the winter months.

The moderate size of the Long-Eared Owl and its long, closely set ear-tufts will readily identify the bird in the field and distinguish it from the Great Horned Owl, our only other owl showing conspicuous ear-tufts. The ear-tufts of the Long-Eared Owl arise from near the middle of the forehead and are not so widely separated as they are in the Great Horned Owl. From the similar Short-Eared Owl it may be distinguished by the longer ear-tufts and (in good light only) by the grayer cast of the plumage.

25

Short-Eared Owl

wwwwwwwwwwwwwwwwwwwwwwwwwwwwwwwwwwwwwwwwwwwwwwwwwwwwwwwwwwwwwwwww

ASIO FLAMMEUS FLAMMEUS

ADULTS Upper parts light yellowish-brown heavily streaked with black. Under parts light straw color, the throat and upper breast widely streaked with dark brown and the lower breast and abdomen finely and narrowly streaked with the same color. Tail, light cinnamon-brown barred with dark brown. Facial discs not prominent. Ear-tufts short and inconspicuous. Iris of eyes, yellow; bill black. Female usually larger than the male.

BODY LENGTH	*WINGSPREAD*
12½ to 17 inches	38 to 44 inches

With a light, bouncing, and apparently effortless flight and irregular wing strokes, the Short-Eared Owl may often be seen, even on a sunny day, flitting and sailing over marsh and meadow, sometimes close to the ground after the fashion of the Marsh Hawk, sometimes high in the air. As it flies, its large rounded head is drawn close to its apparently neckless body, this appearance offering a convenient identificaton mark in the field. It is a bird primarily of the open country, hunting over fields, meadows, bushy pasture lands, salt marshes, sand dunes, and shores. Not infrequently it is observed flying to a considerable distance out over the open water. Its predilection for fenlands, however, is reflected in the names Marsh Owl or Bog Owl by which it is known in some sections of the country. When hunting, the Short-Eared Owl frequently settles on the ground or alights upon a low stub, a pile of hay, or a large stone.

From such points of vantage it watches with motionless vigilance for its prey after the manner of a cat guarding a mousehole. During mild nights the bird often roosts on the ground, but in winter it seeks the shelter of a thick grove of hemlocks, pines, or spruces. Its nest is placed on the ground in a slight depression hidden by grasses, sedges, or small bushes, and is a rather slovenly agglomeration of small sticks and twigs, carelessly lined with grasses, weeds, leaves, and a few feathers. Occasionally a few pairs nest together in a small colony.

The Short-Eared Owl is not very vocal, but in the spring the males utter a series of notes which no doubt fall with a pleasingly seductive cadence upon the ears of the more silent females, a series of *hoots* or *toots* repeated from ten to twenty times and often given while the male birds fly about after the females. The notes are somewhat reminiscent of the hoots uttered by the Great Horned Owl, but are recognizably higher in pitch. Both sexes give voice to a startling, high, squealing cry similar to the yowl of a large cat, *eeeoooo*, or emit notes which snarl or become louder like the syllables *mahyeou*, or *kayeouw*.

Since the Short-Eared Owl is chiefly a bird of open country rather than of thickly wooded areas, the greater part of its mammalian food consists of Field or Meadow Mice together with some Pine Mice, Deer Mice, moles, and shrews. Occasionally a few young rabbits are taken. The insects on which it feeds are chiefly crickets, grasshoppers, and the larger beetles. Some few small birds are devoured such as the Field Sparrow, the Junco, the Fox Sparrow, the Vesper Sparrow, the English Sparrow, and sometimes also the Red-Winged Blackbird, the Robin, and the grackles. There is no question, however, about the bird's very great economic value as a destroyer of small noxious rodents.

The Short-Eared Owl breeds rather rarely in irregularly distributed Northeastern areas. It occurs most frequently along the beaches and over extensive coastal marshes, more commonly in the spring and fall as it migrates to and from its more northern nesting grounds. In the lowlands and marshy regions of New York it is one of the commonest of the owls. In the southern portion of the northeast it becomes increasingly numerous as a winter resident, and I have found it especially numerous during winter in the broad coastal marshes of southern Connecticut and New Jersey, but it is nowhere very common.

Of all the members of our owl family, the Short-Eared Owl is the most widely distributed, since it is found not only over the whole of North America but also in Europe, Asia, the West Indies, Greenland, and the Galapagos Islands.

The Short-Eared Owl may be recognized when perched by its brownish (not grayish) cast of plumage, and by the inconspicuousness of its facial discs. From the Long-Eared Owl it may be distinguished by the absence of the long ear-tufts. When the bird is on the wing its compact, neckless form and bat-like or moth-like flipping proclaim its identity.

26

Northern Barred Owl

wwwwwwwwwwwwwwwwwwwwwwwwwwwwwwwwwwwwwwwwwwwwwwwwwwwwwwwwwwwwwww

STRIX VARIA VARIA

ADULTS Upper parts dark grayish-brown marked with a multitude of small bars of white or yellowish-white. Under parts buffy white, finely crossbarred on the throat and breast, and heavily streaked on the abdomen with dark grayish-brown. The facial discs are concentrically ringed with the last-named color. Ear-tufts absent. Iris of eyes dark brown, almost black; bill yellow. Female slightly larger than the male.

BODY LENGTH	*WINGSPREAD*
17 to 24 inches	40 to 50 inches

Although the Barred Owl is the most numerous of all our large birds of prey and one of the fairly common birds of every extensive woodland, by reason of its secretive nature and nocturnal habits it is nevertheless seldom seen even by those who frequent its haunts. It is a bird of dense wooded swamps, deep forest solitudes, and bosky ravines. Sometimes a pair will be found nesting close by a dwelling in a thick grove of trees where, though their presence may be known, their nesting activities are often brought to completion unobserved by their human neighbors. From such situations their loud, reverberant *hooing* notes boom forth on spring and summer nights with such power that frequently they may be heard for a distance of a mile or more when the air is still. The notes are usually uttered in the earlier half of the night and again in the early morning hours, in monotonous iteration.

Among countryfolk the Barred Owl is sometimes known as the Swamp Owl or more commonly as the Eight-Hooter, from the number of notes in its commonest call. It may be rendered thus: *hoo-hoo, hoo-hoo; hoo-hoo, hoo hoo-aaww*. This may be interpreted into the words, *Oh who are you; Oh who are you-all?* The last note, *you-all*, is slurred downward, an unmistakable cadence which identifies the hooter at once. The notes are more mellow, and slightly higher in pitch than the somewhat similar notes of the Great Horned Owl, but the grouping and the final downward slur is distinctive. Besides these notes the Barred Owl gives vent to numerous croaks, clucks, cackles, snarls, gobblings, gibberings, and to a high-pitched screech heard with dread by many who suppose it is to be the augury of impending death!

> "It was the owl that shrieked, the fatal bellman
> Which gives the stern'st good night."

Many a time in my boyhood has this midnight scream sent me with prickling scalp burrowing down under the security of the bedclothes, even though I knew it was no demon that was lodged outside my bedroom window, but only a soft, fluffy, mild, brown-eyed, harmless old owl.

During the day Barred Owls remain concealed among the dense branches of evergreens or similar protected situations where, however, they are frequently discovered by inquisitive crows and jays which collect in numbers and set up a great *cawing* and *jaying*, swooping down one after another at the luckless owl without the hardihood of attempting to deal him an actual blow.

Barred Owls breed in dense low woodlands or upland forests, often among evergreens, making no nest but depositing their eggs in the cavity of a tree or utilizing the deserted nests of crows, hawks, or squirrels.

More than half of the food of the Barred Owl consists of such mammals as rabbits, chipmunks, squirrels, rats, shrews, moles, and sometimes weasels. The insects eaten are chiefly large beetles, crickets, and grasshoppers. Crayfish, frogs, spiders, and some small fish are also taken. Among the birds devoured by the Barred Owl are the Fox Sparrow, the Vesper Sparrow, and less frequently such larger species as the Ruffed Grouse and the Bob White. Occasionally a solitary individual may raid the poultry yard, destroying young chickens. Pigeons are also sometimes eaten. This owl has the curious habit of preying upon other smaller owls, though not to any great extent. Remains of Screech Owls and other small owls have been found now and then in the stomachs of the birds. But in view of the Barred Owl's destruction of injurious mammals and insects, it is to be viewed as one of our undoubtedly valuable owls and should be accorded all protection.

The Barred Owl is a permanent breeder in the northeastern states wherever there are swampy woods and moderate or heavy forests. It is absent along the coastal zone and in the northern mountains above the elevation of 3,000 feet. It breeds somewhat uncommonly in Massachusetts, Connecticut, Rhode Island, southern New York, and New Jersey, but occurs in increasing numbers in the fall and winter.

This species may be identified by the large round head lacking ear-tufts, the horizontal barring of the breast, the longitudinal streaking of the abdomen, and the deep brown eyes. The eyes of our other owls are yellow.

27

Great Gray Owl

wwwwwwwwwwwwwwwwwwwwwwwwwwwwwwwwwwwwwwwwwwwwwwwwww

STRIX NEBULOSA NEBULOSA

ADULTS Upper parts dark, brownish, slate-gray mottled with white or whitish. Under parts white, heavily streaked on the upper breast, and both sexes heavily streaked and barred on the abdomen with dark, brownish slate-gray. Facial discs white, with about six narrow, concentric rings of black. Iris of eyes and bill yellow. The head and face are much larger in proportion to the body than in our other owls.

BODY LENGTH	*WINGSPREAD*
23½ to 33 inches	48½ to 60 inches

Horrebow devotes the whole of chapter 42 of his *Natural History of Iceland* to the owls of Iceland. The entire chapter reads: "There are no owls of any kind in the island." Similarly one might write an entire chapter on the Great Gray Owl in the northeast area and say only that: "The Great Gray Owl is very rare in the northeastern states," for this owl is only an infrequent winter straggler in the area, and probably does not breed south of the Canadian border. With a wingspread of from four to six feet and a face larger than that of any other of our native owls the bird appears enormous. This apparent size, however, is due to the extremely fluffy character of its feathers. In reality the body is rather small, sometimes even weighing less than that of the Barred Owl. F. T. Jencks says that "it is the most bird for the least substance we ever examined." The great puff of feathers with which its body

is invested is a most effective adaptation for keeping the bird warm in its far northern home, for it ranges in North America as far north as trees will grow and where temperatures under fifty degrees below zero are frequent. In spite of its being so well wrapped up in its "owl-down" quilt, it must often be in the condition of that owl alluded to by Keats:

"St. Agnes' Eve—Ah, bitter chill it was!
The owl for all his feathers was a-cold."

The Great Gray Owl, also called the Spruce Owl, inhabits low forests or high, wooded mountain slopes and rarely straggles southward except when forced to do so by unusually heavy ice and snow.

Little is known in detail concerning the food habits of this owl beyond the fact that it preys upon small mammals such as various species of mice, rabbits, and other similar forms. These constitute the bulk of its food. Small species of birds make up a minor part of its sustenance. When pressed by hunger it probably preys upon any bird or mammal which it can secure. In the United States the species is not numerous enough to exert any appreciable influence upon our agricultural economy.

The Great Gray Owl somewhat resembles the Barred Owl but appears much larger, with very prominent facial discs. Moreover it shows longitudinal streaks on both the breast and the abdomen, and possesses yellow, not brown eyes. In flight its enormous wingspread will distinguish it from any other owl except the Great Horned Owl.

28

Richardson's Owl

~~~~~~

AEGOLIUS FUNEREUS RICHARDSONI

ADULTS Upper parts rich brown, spotted with white; tail narrowly barred four or five times with white. Under parts white, heavily streaked with rich brown. Facial discs grayish-white bordered with brown. Iris of eyes yellow; bill yellow. Females usually slightly larger than the males.

BODY LENGTH	*WINGSPREAD*
8¼ to 12 inches	19 to 24 inches

The name of this rare owl memorializes Sir John Richardson (1767–1865), the Scottish naturalist and traveller who was associated with William Swainson in the publication of the *Fauna Boreali-Americana* in 1829–37.

Richardson's Owl is a bird of the midnight forest. In the Northeast it is abroad only during the hours of twilight and darkness. During the day it remains closely secluded in the dusk of some dense grove of conifers and hence is very seldom seen. Whenever the tramper and watcher in the woods has the good fortune to come upon one of these little owls, he may approach quietly and slowly and sometimes take it in the hand, so bewildered and stupid does the creature seem by day.

Richardson's Owls breed north of our Canadian border, but in winter they descend without regularity into the northeastern states. In the northernmost, heavily forested portions of Maine, New Hampshire, and Vermont they occur in some numbers, less fre-

quently in northern New York. In some places they may become common. Throughout the remainder of the northeastern states they are very rare and irregular during the winter months except as unusually severe winters and the failure of their food supply force them to move southwards into New England (in considerable numbers in the winter of 1922–23).

The notes of the Richardson's Owl I have never heard. They are described as soft, low, liquid, and singly uttered. Sometimes it gives voice to a petulant musical whistle, or to a gentle, subdued, whining scream.

No nest is built by this owl, the eggs being laid in the cavity of a tree or in the deserted nest of a hawk or crow.

Very little is known of the food of the Richardson's Owl, but it is probable that like other owls of its size, general habits, and environment, it feeds upon small mammals, small birds, and large insects.

Richardson's Owl is somewhat similar to the Saw-Whet Owl, but may be distinguished from that species by the yellow bill and the more prominent facial discs, outlined by the heavy brown or black border. From the Screech Owl it may be distinguished by its rounded head, from which ear-tufts are lacking.

29

Saw-Whet Owl

wwwwwwwwwwwwwwwwwwwwwwwwwwwwwwwwwwwwwwwwwwwwwwwwwww

AEGOLIUS ACADICUS ACADICUS

ADULTS Upper parts dark brown sparsely sprinkled with white. Under parts white, with heavy rich brown stripes. Tail crossed by three or four narrow white bars. Facial discs grayish. Iris of eyes yellow; bill black. Female usually slightly larger than male.

BODY LENGTH	*WINGSPREAD*
7 to 8½ inches	17 to 20½ inches

This little midget of an owl, sometimes called also the Acadian Owl, is the smallest of all our birds of prey; it is smaller than the little Screech Owl by an inch or more and even smaller than our common Robin by two inches or more, though its extremely loose and fluffy feathers give it the appearance of a much larger, or rather a much plumper, bird. In flight, too, it seems like a larger bird because of the relatively great spread of its wings, some twenty inches across.

During daylight hours the Saw-Whet Owl remains well concealed amid·thick branches, usually of an evergreen, and in so dull and torpid a state that it may sometimes be caught in the hand. As dusk approaches, however, that time of twilight known among the English as "owl-light," it becomes the veritable embodiment of animated ferocity and energy and is in its rapacious vigor the very antithesis of its daytime self, a perfect little tornado of fluffy feathers, hooked beak, and curved talons, and woe betide any

small woodland creature that happens to be abroad. With surprising courage this diminutive little fury will often attack such relatively large animals as rats, small rabbits, or squirrels, though its favorite fare is White-Footed or Deer Mice. Its hunting is swift and is accomplished in absolute silence because of the soft and downy character of its feathers, which perfectly muffle the quick wing strokes. It is not given to long foraging flights. When disturbed it bursts away from its haunts with a haphazard, irregular flight quite characteristic of the bird and calling to mind the flight of a flushed Woodcock.

The common note of the Saw-Whet Owl, from which the bird derives its name, is a penetrating, rasping call given in triads and resembling the sound made by the filing of a large saw, *screek-kaw, screek-kaw, screek-kaw*. Other notes are a series of liquid *cooing* sounds, a variety of clucks and gurgles, and a faint scream like the protestations of a house cat whose tail is being pulled.

The Saw-Whet Owl probably occurs among us more commonly than is ordinarily supposed, since its voice carries only for relatively short distances and since, moreover, it is diminutive in size and remains concealed by day.

Saw-Whets breed in low wet woodlands, laying their eggs in the deserted holes of woodpeckers, often those of the Hairy Woodpecker or of the Flicker, or in any cavities which offer sufficient protection. Sometimes the eggs are laid in a decayed stub; or the deserted nest of a Crow, Mourning Dove, small hawk, or squirrel is pressed into service, and I once found a nest in a cleft in the side of a mountain cave. Occasionally the eggs are laid on a bare surface without any bed, though sometimes they are cushioned on a shallow layer of feathers, grasses, mosses, or weed stems.

The little Saw-Whet Owl includes more insects in its diet than does any other native owl, these forms being taken almost entirely during the summer months. Almost any sort of insect large enough to come into the owl's ken is eagerly devoured. While the bird is with us in the winter, various species of mice such as Pine Mice,

Deer Mice, and Meadow Mice, together with some chipmunks form the greater proportion of its food. Small birds are very rarely taken and form only a small percentage of the yearly diet. The large number of mice destroyed by this little owl indicate that it is a species of considerable economic value.

In the northern portions of Maine, New Hampshire, Vermont, and New York, the Saw-Whet Owl is a rather uncommon permanent resident, but a somewhat common migrant and winter visitant. Throughout the rest of New England it breeds very rarely, but occurs without regularity more commonly in winter. In the southern part of the northeast it is found as a rare late fall and winter visitor. It is not, strictly speaking, migratory, but wanders about in an unpredictable fashion after the breeding season is over, and is thus irregular both in its annual and in its geographical distribution, being fairly common in one locality one year and rare or absent the next. When unusually severe winters bring deep snows and heavy sheaths of ice to its northern breeding grounds, the bird is forced southwards and at such times become quite abundant there, as during the winter of 1922 and 1923.

The Saw-Whet Owl might possibly be confused with the Screech Owl were it not for its plain head, which lacks the ear-tufts. Its dark brown upper parts contrast with the bright chestnut brown longitudinal streaks of the upper parts. No other owl is similarly marked.

30

Eastern Screech Owl

wwwwwwwwwwwwwwwwwwwwwwwwwwwwwwwwwwwwwwwwwwwwwwwwwwwwwwww

OTUS ASIO NAEVIUS

ADULTS In the gray phase: Upper parts brownish-gray delicately streaked with black and finely flecked with yellowish-white. Under parts white sparsely marked with broad streaks of black and finely barred with the same color. In the brown phase: Gray everywhere replaced with reddish-brown. Facial discs not prominent. Ear-tufts prominent and rising from nearer the sides of the head, and not directly over the eyes. Iris of eyes yellow; bill yellowish. Female larger than the male.

BODY LENGTH	WINGSPREAD
6½ to 10 inches	18 to 24 inches

This owl may be said to be our only "town dweller." Owls as a rule are birds of swamps, forests, and the wilder recesses, but this little species occurs in the suburbs of towns, in small villages, and in farming districts generally, for it seems to take kindly to man's occupation of the land and to breed and thrive in the vicinity of his dwellings in spite of the injudicious warfare which is sometimes waged against it. Screech Owls make their simple nests of sticks, plant rubbish, and a few feathers, in crevices in deserted outbuildings, sometimes even in nesting-boxes intended for Flickers, more commonly in cavities of trees in old apple orchards, or in deserted woodpecker holes in moderate and open woodlands. During the day it keeps itself closely concealed among thick foliage or in a tree cavity. Here, however, it is sometimes discovered by a flock of smaller birds which subject the poor torpid creature to an

agitated and clamorous persecution, toward which the object of all this undignified and unprovoked attack maintains a complete and aristocratic indifference.

The Screech Owl is one of the most nocturnal of our owls. At dusk it sallies forth and may be seen flying silently about farm buildings, haystacks, and piles of brush in its unremitting quest for mice and other nocturnal animals or hovering about vine-covered walls in search of English Sparrows which commonly roost in such situations.

The Screech Owl's note is the most plaintively sweet and doleful of all bird utterances, a tremulous wailing cry, suggestive of the prolonged, subdued whinny of a small horse, quavering and sepulchral in character and yet with a pleasing musical quality. To some ears it is a thoroughly agreeable sound, a sound inducive of a pleasurable melancholy; to others its weird and ghostly tremolo is prophetic of disaster or death. It may be written, *Whe-e-e-e-e-o-o-o-oh*, with a slight fall of pitch at its close. The bird rarely screeches, and hence the name Screech Owl, taken from the European bird, is inappropriate to our species. The bird is sometimes called the Shivering Owl, Red Owl, and Cat Owl.

Small mammals, insects, and small birds form the bulk of the food of this active and very common little owl. Among the mammals upon which it feeds may be mentioned the House Mouse, the Meadow or Field Mouse, the Pine Mouse, and the Deer Mouse. Moles, shrews, and bats are also taken and occasionally Flying Squirrels, chipmunks, and rats. By far the greater proportion of its mammal diet consists, however, of the smaller forms such as mice. Small birds also form a considerable percentage of the food of the Screech Owl and are taken chiefly in winter when insects are at their minimum. Among the birds devoured are large numbers of English Sparrows where these are numerous, as they are about farm buildings, and lesser numbers of such species as the Junco, the House Wren, the Chipping Sparrow, the Savanna Sparrow, the Tree Sparrow, the Horned Lark, and the Bluebird. Some of these are young birds taken from the nest, for occasionally a Screech Owl reaches down into the cavity of a hole-nesting species such as the Bluebird or the House Wren and picks out the nestlings. Sometimes relatively large birds are taken, for example, Woodcocks or Quails, though this is rare. During the summer months large quantities of insects are eaten. Indeed during this season the insects in the diet may reach nearly 50 per cent of the whole. Any large forms—beetles, grasshoppers, crickets, cutworms—are welcome additions. May Beetles (June Bugs) are taken in large quantities on warm summer nights. Frogs and snakes are eagerly devoured, as are salamanders, fishes, and crayfish. Spiders, earthworms, millipedes, snails, and slugs are eaten whenever they are found.

Screech Owls are undesirable in a bird sanctuary or on grounds where nesting-boxes are inhabited by Bluebirds, Wrens, Flickers, Chickadees, Nuthatches, Downy Woodpeckers, and other hole-nesting species. In general, however, because of their destruction of harmful rodents and insect pests, they are to be regarded as a beneficial species and accorded every protection.

These little owls are only fairly common permanent residents in the northern parts of the area and are absent entirely among the higher mountains, but as one goes farther south into Massachusetts, southern New York, Connecticut, Rhode Island, and New Jersey, they become progressively more numerous except locally among high hills and deeply wooded areas and along the open beaches and extensive coastal marshes.

In either the brown or the gray phase of its plumage the Screech Owl is readily identifiable by its small size and prominent ear-tufts.

31

Great Horned Owl

~~~~~~

BUBO VIRGINIANUS VIRGINIANUS

ADULTS Upper parts mottled with light brownish, yellowish, white, and black. Throat white, the rest of the under parts yellowish-white finely and heavily barred with black. The upper breast bears about six heavy irregular black streaks. Facial discs light brown edged with black. Ear-tufts long and prominent. Iris of eyes deep yellow; bill large and black.

BODY LENGTH	*WINGSPREAD*
Male, 18 to 23 inches	Male, 35 to 52 inches
Female, 22 to 25 inches	Female, 53 to 60 inches

The more unsettled parts of our country where impenetrable swamps, deep lowland forests, and wild wooded mountain and hillsides abound are the common domains of the Great Horned Owls. Seldom are they found close to human dwellings. Unlike many of our native birds, they shun civilization and retreat before man's progressive occupation of the land. This owl is the one most commonly called the "Hoot Owl" by hunters. Its notes are all on the same pitch, deep and booming, and are the lowest notes heard in the forest. Usually they are uttered without any definite rhythm, as *hoo, hoo, hoo, hoo, hoo;* but sometimes they are grouped or accented thus, *hoo, hoo; hoo-hoo,* or *hoo hoo hoo hoo-hoo.* In addition to these notes the bird infrequently emits a loud terrifying scream, as of a being in the direst anguish, a sound which if once heard in the midnight forest is never forgotten.

The Great Horned Owl is the most fearless of all our birds of prey, swooping and striking its eight long, curved talons into almost any moving object which attracts its attention. Reports have been made of its attacks upon the Bald Eagle, the Porcupine, large dogs, and even man himself. It makes a common prey of the Skunk with utter disregard of its terrific weapon, for owls, like other birds, possess almost no sense of smell. The owl's body, moreover, presents no bare surfaces of skin, and the eyeballs can be covered with the protective nictitating membranes; hence there is no part of the owl's body upon which the Skunk's fiery excretion can exert its vitriolic effect.

A remarkable instance of the voracious ferocity of the Great Horned Owl is given by Leo Luttringer, Game Commissioner of Pennsylvania: "The keeper of our local zoo (at Harrisburg) recently placed two Barn Owls (*Tyto alba pratincola*) in the same cage with two Great Horned Owls (*Bubo virginianus virginianus*). The following morning when he went to look after the birds, he found the two Great Horned Owls, but only the feet of the Barn Owls. No other creature could possibly have gained entrance to the cage, so it is deduced that the larger owls ate the smaller ones."

More than half of the prey of the Great Horned Owl consists of such mammals as woodchucks, skunks, minks, weasels, opossums, rabbits, hares, squirrels, chipmunks, rats, mice, shrews, and moles. In many cases only the brains of the larger creatures are eaten. Rats often form a very large proportion of the mammal food. Occasionally a domestic cat will be struck and its brains devoured. Among the larger birds which fall prey to the Horned Owl may be listed the Barred Owl (and other smaller species of owls), hawks, game birds of all kinds, chickens and other domestic birds, doves, Crows (of which this owl seems particularly fond), Flickers or Yellow Hammers, and other smaller birds. Crayfish, fish, large beetles, grasshoppers, crickets, frogs, and reptiles are also eaten. It is the most rapacious of all our birds of prey with the possible exceptions of the Cooper's Hawk and the Goshawk. In the wilder parts of its

146

range the Great Horned Owl forms one of the necessary and beneficial factors in the balance of nature, and in such situations it is valuable on economic grounds; but where occasionally it occurs in the vicinity of farms or in game preserves, it may become a detriment. It should never be shot in the wilderness, for in the wilderness it is in its own domain where man is decidedly the unprovoked aggressor. It should be killed only where it is seriously interfering with man's designs in the cultivation of his necessary foodstuffs.

The Great Horned Owl is distributed all over the Northeast when breeding, but is not common except in the wilder, more mountainous, and more densely forested regions of the north. It is rarely encountered in southern Connecticut, southern New York, or the farm areas of New Jersey, and is even scarcer in Rhode Island.

The Great Horned Owl is our only large owl possessing ear-tufts. When the head is held very erect, the bird's broad white collar is conspicuous. In flight it may be identified by its great size, its large round head, and neckless appearance.

32

Arctic Horned Owl

~~~~~~

BUBO VIRGINIANUS WAPACUTHU

ADULTS Similar to the Great Horned Owl but everywhere paler, sometimes almost white. Pattern of the markings is also similar.

BODY LENGTH	*WINGSPREAD*
Male, 18 to 23 inches	Male, 35 to 52 inches
Female, 22 to 25 inches	Female, 53 to 60 inches

The haunts, habits and dietary of this subspecies of the Great Horned Owl are similar to those of its more familiar congener. Breeding in north central Canada, it reaches the northeastern states only occasionally when the compulsion of unusually severe winters in its northern home forces it southward. It may be differentiated from the Snowy Owl by the presence of the prominent ear-tufts.

33

Labrador Horned Owl

~~~~~~

BUBO VIRGINIANUS HETEROCNEMIS

ADULTS Similar to the Great Horned Owl, but everywhere much darker, and more heavily barred below, sometimes appearing almost black-breasted.

BODY LENGTH	WINGSPREAD
Male, 18 to 23 inches	Male, 35 to 52 inches
Female, 22 to 25 inches	Female, 53 to 60 inches

As the Arctic Horned Owl is the *white* form of horned owl, so the Labrador is the *dark* form. The bird breeds in Labrador, northern Quebec, Newfoundland, and Nova Scotia and descends rarely into northern New England in exceptionally rigorous winters. Its habits are similar to those of the Great Horned and Arctic Horned Owls.

34

Snowy Owl

wwwwwwwwwwwwwwwwwwwwwwwwwwwwwwwwwwwwwwwwwwwwwwwwwwwwwwwwwwwwwww

NYCTEA SCANDIACA

ADULT MALE   White, barred with grayish-brown, slightly more on the head, back wings, and tail. Facial discs white. Eartufts lacking. Iris of eyes yellow; bill black.

ADULT FEMALE   Similar to the male, but more heavily barred. Face, throat, middle of breast, and abdomen, pure unmarked white. Somewhat larger than the male.

BODY LENGTH	*WINGSPREAD*
20 to 27 inches	54 to 66 inches

The Snowy Owls are not at all common in the United States, being creatures of the arctic north wherever there is bare ground. They do not breed south of the Canadian border and in the northeastern states occur only as rare spring and fall migrants, and also as rare winter visitants. Locally and irregularly in the northernmost part of the Northeast, they may sometimes be fairly common, especially along the coast. In severe winters they descend in considerable numbers into the northern states. Thus some of the heavy invasions of Snowy Owls that have occurred in New England and New York have been during the winters of 1876–77, 1882–83, 1889–90, 1892–93, 1896–97, 1901–02, 1905–06, 1917–18, 1930–31, and 1934–35. Other names are Arctic Owl and White Owl.

The Snowy Owl hunts both by day and during the hours of morning and evening twilight, sitting motionless on a low stub, large

stone, or tuft of grass, or on a slight hillock where it can scan the surrounding country for its lowly prey, for it is not a bird of forests but of open ground. Seldom is it found far from the treeless country along the seacoast, where it occurs on beaches, in salt marshes, or on the swampy swales and flats along rivers and tidal estuaries. Sometimes but less commonly it may be seen farther inland in meadows, in open fields, or in old pastures.

While with us it is a silent bird. I have never heard its voice, which is said to be shrill, whining, and tremulous.

It is reported nesting in treeless regions, in a depression in the ground, or in the cavity of a cliff.

Even though the bird is unusually well provided with feathers, yet it seems to be singularly susceptible to changes in temperature. Vennor says, "It has always seemed unaccountable to me that the Snowy Owl should at all be influenced by the cold. His plumage is most wonderfully adapted for the most inclement weather we can conceive of, being thick, elastic, and closely matted or interwoven. Anyone who has ever attempted to skin one of these birds will without hesitation bear me out in this statement. It seems an endless task to get beyond the feathers; and even when we have succeeded in parting the outer and inner portions of the plumage, we still find a thick matting of white down which has to be plucked off before the skin is finally exposed. Again when we remove the skin we find the whole body encased in a thick coating of yellow fat, so that, as I have stated, it is difficult to conceive of any cold severe enough to penetrate such a covering."

The food of the Snowy Owl consists of more than 50 per cent of mammals, and more than 25 per cent of small birds, with a relatively small percentage of large birds. The mammals devoured are chiefly Lemmings found in its far northern home and some species of mice. In the northeast it feeds mostly on Meadow Mice, Deer Mice, rats, and any other small mammals which it can capture such as shrews, minks, weasels, rabbits, and the like. The birds taken by the Snowy Owl include Ptarmigans in the north, gulls, ducks, grouse,

152

and very infrequently domestic fowls. Fish are often included in its diet, and under the severer stresses of winter the bird has been known to gorge itself with carrion.

The Snowy Owl is our only white owl and can scarcely be mistaken for any other species. Its large round head possesses no ear-tufts.

35

Hawk Owl

wwwwwwwwwwwwwwwwwwwwwwwwwwwwwwwwwwwwwwwwwwwwwwwwwwwww

SURNIA ULULA CAPAROCH

ADULTS Upper parts dark grayish-brown, the top of the head and neck finely speckled with white. Tertials heavily spotted with white. The tail bears about seven fine white bars and is long for an owl, being about half as long as the body and rounded at the tip. Sides of neck and upper breast streaked with dark grayish-brown; breast and abdomen white thickly barred with brown. Facial discs whitish bordered on the sides with black. Eyes rather small for an owl, their irises yellow. Bill yellow, set off by a blackish patch underneath. Ear-tufts absent. Female usually slightly larger than the male.

BODY LENGTH	*WINGSPREAD*
14½ to 17½ inches	31 to 34 inches

The Hawk Owl, as its name suggests, is in appearance at least partly a hawk and partly an owl. Its long tail and relatively small eyes suggest a hawk, as does also its habit of perching in full daylight on some exposed branch where in motionless patience it watches for passing rodents. In perching the bird inclines its body forward at an angle, though it occasionally assumes the more upright position common to owls. It is not at all a wary creature and may be approached quite closely before it takes wing. When disturbed and driven from its perch it drops suddenly in a short downward curve, just clearing the tree-tops and bushes and flies off with an easy, flexible flight, more hawk-like than owl-like, exhibiting its

longish tail and pointed falcon-like wings. Its high squealing flight-calls remind one of the cries of the Osprey or Fish Hawk, sounding like the syllables *pi-reek, pi-reek*. The bird possesses a large repertory of other notes including whines, whistles, and shrill screams.

The Hawk Owl nests in coniferous forests, laying its eggs amid a few feathers in a hollow stump or in a hole in a tree, or more rarely in a pocket in a cliff or in an old deserted hawk's nest.

The food of the Hawk Owl consists chiefly of Meadow Mice, similar small species, and Lemmings. Some rabbits, hares, weasels, and grouse are also taken. Little is known in detail of the dietary of this species, but it is probable that its destruction of mice and Lemmings renders it worthy of the protection of agriculturists and conservationists generally.

The Hawk Owl is not a nesting bird in the northeast, but breeds to the north beyond the Canadian border. In northern Maine, New Hampshire, and New York it may be locally, at least, a fairly common winter visitant, but in general in Maine, New Hampshire, Vermont, New York, and Massachusetts it is only of rare and irregular occurrence in the fall and winter. In Rhode Island, Connecticut, and New Jersey the bird is to be found only very infrequently as an accidental winter straggler.

This is our only owl with entire under parts thickly crossbarred. The white area on the throat is much smaller than on that of the Great Horned Owl. Its owl-like head and body and hawk-like tail are diagnostic. When perched, the bird frequently pumps its tail after the manner of the Sparrow Hawk. Because of its habit of hunting by daylight, the bird is frequently called the Day Owl.

CLASSIFICATION OF THE BIRDS
OF PREY OF NORTHEASTERN
NORTH AMERICA

I. The Diurnal Birds of Prey

ORDER FALCONIFORMES

II. The Nocturnal Birds of Prey

ORDER STRIGIFORMES (Owls)

Family *i*: TYTONIDAE

Family *ii*: STRIGIDAE

Bibliography

THE *list below contains some of the best nontechnical books and booklets suitable for more extended reading in the subject of birds of prey or usable as identification guides to these birds in the field.*

ALLEN, A. A., *Key to the Nests of Summer Resident Birds of Northeast North America*, Slingerland-Comstock Co., Ithaca, N. Y., 1922.

ALLEN, A. A., *The Book of Bird Life* (2nd edition), D. Van Nostrand Co., Princeton, N. J.

BENT, A. C., "Life Histories of North American Birds of Prey" (in his *Life Histories of North American Birds*, U. S. National Museum, Washington, D. C.), 1919–1947.

BLANCHAN, NELTJE, *Birds That Hunt and Are Hunted*, Doubleday, Doran, N. Y., 1905.

BROUN, M., *Hawks Aloft*, Dodd Mead Co., N. Y., 1949.

CHAPMAN, F. M., *Handbook of the Birds of Eastern North America*, D. Appleton Co., N. Y., 1932.

CRAIGHEAD, J. J., and CRAIGHEAD, F. C., *Hawks, Owls, and Wildlife*, Wildlife Management Institute, Washington, D. C., 1946.

EATON, E. H., *Birds of New York*, N. Y. State Museum, Albany, N. Y., 1910–1914.

FISHER, A. K., *Hawks and Owls of the United States*, U. S. Department of Agriculture, Bulletin No. 3, Washington, D. C., 1893.

FISHER, A. K., *Hawks and Owls from the Standpoint of the Farmer*, U. S. Biological Survey, Circular No. 61, Washington, D. C., 1907.

FORBUSH, E. H., *Useful Birds and Their Protection*, State Board of Agriculture, Boston, Mass., 1907.

FORBUSH, E. H., *Birds of Massachusetts and Other New England States*, 3 vols., State Board of Agriculture, Boston, Mass., 1925–1929. Volume II includes the birds of prey.

FORBUSH, E. H., and MAY, J. B., *Natural History of the Birds of Eastern and Central North America*, Houghton, Mifflin Co., Boston, Mass., 1939.

GRISCOM, L., *Birds of the New York City Region*, American Museum of Natural History, N. Y., 1923.

HAUSMAN, L. A., *Field Book of Eastern Birds*, G. P. Putnam's Sons, N. Y., 1946.

HAUSMAN, L. A., *The Hawks of New Jersey*, N. J. Agricultural Experiment Station, Rutgers University, New Brunswick, N. J., 1927.

HAUSMAN, L. A., *The Owls of New Jersey*, N. J. Agricultural Experiment Station, Rutgers University, New Brunswick, N. J., 1941.

HEADSTROM, R., *Birds' Nests*, Ives Washburn, Inc., N. Y., 1949.

HERRICK, F. H., *The American Eagle*, D. Appleton-Century Co., N. Y., 1934.

HENDERSON, JUNIUS, *The Practical Value of Birds*, Macmillan Co., N. Y., 1927.

HOFFMAN, R., *Guide to the Birds of New England and Eastern New York*, Houghton Mifflin Co., Boston, Mass., 1904.

LEWIS, J. B., *Sight and Scent in the Turkey Vulture*, in The Auk, vol. 45, pp. 467–470, 1928.

MAY, J. B., *The Hawks of North America*, National Audubon Society, N. Y., 1935.

Nature Lovers' Library, "Birds of America," The University Society, N. Y., 1917, 3 vols. Volume II includes the birds of prey.

National Geographic Magazine, "American Birds of Prey," in the December, 1920, issue.

PETERSON, R. T., *Field Guide to the Birds*, Houghton Mifflin Co., 1947.

POUGH, R. H., *All the Birds of Eastern and Central North America* (Audubon Bird Guides), Doubleday and Co., 1957.

POUGH, R. H., *Eastern Land Birds* (Audubon Bird Guide), Doubleday and Co., 1946.

REED, C. A., *Land Birds East of the Rockies*, Doubleday and Co., 1951.

SNYDER, L. L., *The Hawks and Owls of Ontario*, Royal Museum of Zoology, Toronto, 1932.

STONE, W., *Bird Studies at Old Cape May*, Academy of Natural Sciences, Philadelphia, 1937.

VENNOR, H. G., *Our Birds of Prey: The Eagles, Hawks and Owls of Canada*, Montreal, 1876.

WEED, C. M., and DEARBORN, N., *Birds in Relation to Man*, J. B. Lippincott Co., Philadelphia, 1935.

INDEX OF VERNACULAR NAMES OF BIRDS OF PREY